TABLE OF CONTENTS

Silvia Hartmann's

Adventures In EFT

Foreword By Gary Craig

6th Edition
January 2003

DragonRising.com
18 Marlow Avenue
Eastbourne
East Sussex BN22 8SJ
United Kingdom

Adventures In EFT
© Silvia Hartmann 1999/2003
Sixth Edition January 2003
ISBN 1-873483 63 5

DragonRising.com
18 Marlow Avenue
Eastbourne BN22 8SJ
United Kingdom
www.DragonRising.com

Printed and bound in England by Antony Rowe Ltd, Chippenham, Witlshire

---

Caution:

The treatment procedures in this Self Help book are not intended to replace medical or psychiatric treatment.

Readers with medical or psychiatric conditions should consult with their appropriate health practitioner and start their EFT treatment under the supervision and guidance of a certified practitioner of Meridian Therapies.

FOREWORD BY GARY CRAIG, FOUNDER OF EFT

You and I should send Silvia Hartmann a basket filled with gratitude for bringing EFT to life on these pages.

Using her engaging writing style, she describes this remarkable healing technique in compelling terms for both everyday citizens and those in the healing professions.

She blends her extensive knowledge of other fields with EFT to bring you a book that is useful, entertaining and practical.

We are on the ground floor of a Healing High-Rise and EFT is lighting the way. It represents a paradigm shift in the healing field which requires fresh thinking if we are to use it to its fullest extent.

Who would have thought that this simple procedure of tapping on various energy meridian points would allow healing where everything else had failed? Who would have thought that years of healing sessions for specific traumas, phobias, anger, guilt and grief could be reduced to a few minutes? Who would have thought that reducing one's emotional load so easily would often have profound effects on physical ailments such as pain, headaches and breathing problems?

I've been doing these procedures since 1991 on behalf of hundreds of people. Through my videotape series and seminars I have trained thousands of EFT practitioners throughout the world (including Silvia) who are performing these miracles daily.

However, we haven't reached perfection yet and we don't get 100% results. Nonetheless, EFT works remarkably well most of the time and is creating profound effects around the globe.

Silvia's masterful work is your opportunity to learn about it.

Gary Craig

P.S. If you would like to learn even more about EFT, please visit our extensive web site at http://www.emofree.com

Welcome To EFT!

In the autumn of 1998, three little letters kept cropping up all over my hypnotherapy related Internet groups - EFT.

Apparently, this stood for Emotional Freedom Techniques and people were simply raving about it.

It got so bad that the moderators forbade mention of the technique because discussions on its use were monopolising lists that were originally set up for hypnotherapists, neuro-linguists and personal development strategies in general.

I knew some of the people who were so excited and enthusiastic about this new thing and couldn't help but wonder what on earth could be so amazing. Eventually, I visited the website www.emofree.com and that same night, I phoned the States and ordered a copy of the basic course - 11 videos, 4 audio tapes and a thick manual.

When it arrived, I sat down with a cup of coffee, as open a mind as I could consciously manage, and when the example treatments began, I tapped along to learn what it felt like and to familiarise myself with the points and the procedure.

An hour later, I had accessed a severely repressed traumatic time - the death of my father.

I had touched the intense pain I had been carrying for a long seven years, I had been absolutely horrified by the realisation that time had not even begun to heal this at all, and I had released the pain through the tapping, reaching a state of brilliance and clarity; a state of awareness; a release so profound that I cannot convey what this was like or how it subsequently affected me to you in mere words.

I knew then that all I had heard about this technique was true.

It was as profound and powerful as they had said it was.

This really, truly worked.

Since that moment, my life has not been the same again.

As a therapist, since then I have been able to literally make the lame walk and the blind see. I have had more thank you letters in the past year than I got in 15 years before.

As a teacher, I have been able to allow my students to learn at a level they never thought possible.

As an individual, I have gained a profoundly new elegance of life. I have discovered new skills and abilities I never thought I possessed, and those I already used, have become supercharged.

As a mother, I have been able to calm my children, to support them in a way that was previously unimaginable, and to help them permanently overcome perceived limitations and moments of loss of faith.

What more can I say?

I sincerely hope that this book will be the starting point of your journey of discovery of self through this most wonderful of mind/body healing tools.

God Bless EFT.

Silvia Hartmann
August 1999

WELCOME TO ADVENTURES, 6TH EDITION

It has now been four years since I first discovered EFT, and nearly three years since the original introduction above was written.

This is the 6th edition of Adventures, a special version designed and expanded to help to spread the word around the World about EFT and the new Meridian Energy Therapies, touching one person at a time who then pass it along to their friends, family, clients.

After four years of virtually "living with" EFT, I still use it when the need arises, and so do my friends, famous therapists in their own rights, who started out on this true adventure around the same time.

I'm still amazed sometimes just how effective it is and how much you can do with it. I'm amazed at what we have learned, not just about our own lives, personalities, choices but also about how memory, mind and emotion really work.

There are many meridian energy based therapies now, and every week there are new ideas, new protocols, new additions, new discoveries – it is truly extraordinary to be here and watch the development of this whole new field of mind, body healing and to be so lucky and privileged to be a part of it, to help shape it and to contribute to it.

But at the end of the day, as individuals, when we're in a panic or it all gets too much – yes, it still happens! – we turn to basic EFT, time and time again, because it is simply so very reliable, so easy to use and incredibly helpful in more ways than you can imagine just yet.

EFT has absolutely become a part of our lives, a trusted and helpful companion that will stand by our side if only we remember to call on it.

I have learned a lot in the past four years and many of these things are written down elsewhere.

Adventures in EFT is always going to be about EFT and not about anything else.

EFT is an incredible tool with incredible flexibility built in and I am glad that I studied it as deeply as I did, because the more I used it, the more uses for it did I find and the more impressed with the basic protocol I became.

If you are a "newbie" or if you are an old experienced hand at METs by now, it doesn't matter.

To return to the basics and to learn the basics properly is the greatest gift you can give yourself, whether it be in typing, playing the piano or in using Meridian Energy Therapies.

This is a truly great technique – make it your own in every way and I'll promise you, it will deliver much, much more than you ever thought possible.

With my best wishes to you and all those you share this with,

Silvia Hartmann

January 2003

PART I - LEARNING EFT

1. How To Use This Book

In Part I, I'm going to walk you through the basic technique of EFT.

It is extremely simple, and extremely easy to learn.

Its effects are also extreme - you should have a profound response if you follow the instructions carefully. If you do not, I would suggest that you allow yourself to seek out an EFT workshop, a practitioner or buy the basic EFT Practitioner's video tape set. Only a few in a hundred people fail to get results with EFT if it is applied properly, perhaps even less than that. Chances are that with a little bit of extra help you too will be able to access the tremendous resources on offer, some of which I discuss in Part III. I have grouped the ideas for EFT application alphabetically, but you can read them as though they were chapters which follow one another.

In Part IV, you will find a number of "EFT extensions" – strategies designed to support the basic EFT process and to make it even more flexible.

In Part V, I have given a short explanation of terms used in EFT and their meanings so you can look them up at any time during the reading of this book.

In Part VI, you will find some of the currently available resources and "further learning" possibilities you can explore at your leisure.

Let us start now with a very brief ...

2. History of EFT

The principles behind EFT were discovered by Dr Roger Callahan, a clinical psychologist of over 40 years experience, who had made it his life's work to find ways to cure people of unfounded fears, phobias, and anxieties, because he himself had suffered from these since childhood.

Like any true explorer, he left no stone unturned, and finally came across some techniques, which proved to have startling repercussions.

In the much told story, he had a client named Mary who suffered from a severe phobia of water - she couldn't look at any bodies of water and found bathing highly traumatic, even if there was only a couple of inches of water in the tub. He had been working with her for 18 months, using absolutely anything and everything standard psychology and even non-standard psychology, such as hypnosis, had to offer, but she still remained afraid to death of water.

During one session, he asked her to tap under the eye, which is an important acupuncture/ acupressure/meridian point, and the fear just disappeared - instantaneously. It has never returned, and the treatment took place 16 years ago.

Dr Callahan called his discovery Thought Field Therapy, on the grounds that thoughts related to the energy field in the body, and that changing this energy field by tapping on the meridian points could release negative emotions rapidly and easily.

He refined and researched his method, and today TFT and its descendants are the subject of serious scientific study and have already gained wide-spread acceptance.

TFT treatments are based on what is called **algorithms** - specific sequences of tapping points to relieve specific problems.

One of Dr Callahan's students, Gary Craig, a Stanford Engineer, came up with the brilliant idea to just tap all the points for every presenting problem - there are, after all, only 13 of them, so whichever point or points were the correct ones, they would always be covered by default.

This is an engineering technique used when a fault cannot be found – everything is replaced and the concept is known as "total redundancy".

He thereby managed to create a technique that EVERYONE can learn to use very easily and very quickly, and which does not require special diagnostic training, therapy training, or even any knowledge of the body's energy system whatever.

Gary Craig called his streamlined version "EFT - Emotional Freedom Technique".

I will take this opportunity to express my tremendous admiration for Dr Callahan who has given the world a legacy to be proud of; and my tremendous gratitude to Gary Craig, who has made this technique accessible to every man and every woman in the street.

If you are interested in learning more about the thinking, the science and advanced therapeutical applications behind EFT, I cannot recommend too highly that you should engage in the trainings available in the field. At the end of this book, there are recommendations for further learnings, trainings, courses and books.

Here, we are only concerned with talking about the basic technique and all the wonderful things you can do with EFT, so let's now press on and find out what EFT is all about, and how it works.

3. How EFT Works

EFT rests on a theory that is called:

"The Discovery Statement"

This is very important and central to the understanding of EFT, so here is the Discovery Statement:

> **The Cause Of ALL Negative Emotions**
>
> **Is A Disruption In The Bodys Energy System.**

It used to be held in psychotherapy that a negative emotion was caused by a negative or traumatic memory or event.

Every time, this memory was accessed or "lit up" as a result of a thought or an environmental reminder of some kind, the negative emotion was experienced:

"Memory => Negative Emotion"

in a simple

"Cause => Effect"

relationship.

Dr Callahan, on the other hand, discovered that there was a step in between the memory/thought and the negative emotion, and this was **a disruption in the smooth flowing of the energy through the meridian system.**

18

So instead of the memory or thought causing the negative emotion, according to the discovery statement, the process is more like this:

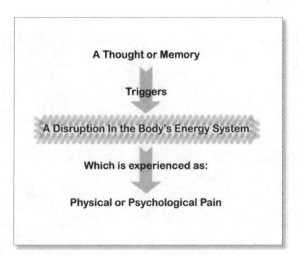

Thereby, instead of trying to undo the thoughts or memories in some way, which has been attempted by millions in therapy for many years and with highly unpredictable results, the energy based therapies directly intervene in the intermediate step - when the disruption in the energy system has been calmed and relieved, the person experiences no further pain or negative emotions from the original memory or thought.

As you will see, this simple yet profound discovery doesn't only make perfect sense, it has also proven itself in practice - there are thousands of therapists like myself all across the world, daily relieving clients of all kinds of long standing problems using variations on this idea, successfully, predictably, time and time again.

Theory and conscious understanding is all good and well, but you don't really begin to appreciate the truth of how amazing and wonderful EFT is - until you have experienced it for yourself.

In a moment, we're going to learn how to do basic EFT, and you can pick any limitation, fear, traumatic memory that bothers you and try it out for yourself.

4. The Technique And How To Use It

a. Points & Tapping

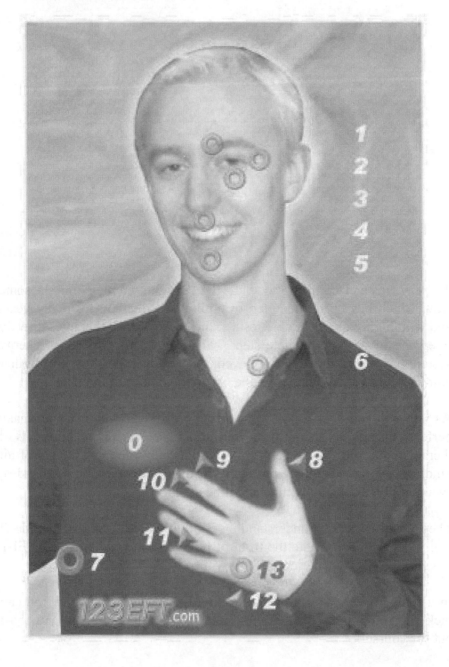

EFT uses 14 major meridian points, which are generally at the start or the end of a major body meridian. Here they are:

0 = The Sore Spot - On your chest where you would pin a medal or a brooch. Gently push with your fingertips to find an area that feels tender, rather than sore.

1 = Start Of The Eyebrow - Where the bone behind your eyebrow turns into the bridge of your nose.

2 = Corner Of The Eye - On the bone in the corner of your eye.

3 = Under The Eye - On the bone just below your eye, in line with your pupil if you look straight ahead.

4 = Under The Nose - Between you nose and your upper lip

5 = Under The Mouth - In the indentation between your chin and your lower lip

6 = Collarbone - In the angle formed by your collarbone and the breastbone

7 = Under Arm - in line with a man's nipples on the side of the body

8 = Thumb - all finger points are on the side of the finger, in line with the nail bed.

9 = Index Finger, 10 = Middle Finger, 11 = Little Finger

12 = Karate Chop Point - on the side of your hand, roughly in line with your life line.

13 = Gamut Point - just behind and between the knuckles of your ring and little finger.

Take a moment now to find and touch each point in turn. You may notice that some feel slightly different from others, or you may not.

When you get to work on various issues, you will feel that some of the points "feel" differently when you tap them, and you will notice that the shift or release will occur with one or more points, depending on the reason for using the technique at the time.

In EFT, these points are stimulated by tapping on them.

Try now tapping the point under your eye, with your index or index and middle fingers, quite rapidly about seven to nine times or as many times as it takes for you to take a normal breath in and out. The strength of tapping should be comfortable, but you should be able to feel a resonance from the tapping spreading out across a reasonable part of that side of your face.

I have noticed that different people have different speeds of tapping. We generally show a tapping speed in line with the rhythm of "Jingle Bells". In spite of this, some people develop a kind of woodpecker action after a while, and others tap quite slowly. I would suggest that what feels right to you probably is right for you. *See also Rhythm & Percussion In Tapping Treatments in the Addendum.*

For practice, turn back to the diagram and tap all the points from the Eyebrow to the Karate Chop point now just to get the feel of doing it.

b. Contacting The Problem

In my opinion, the one thing that makes the biggest difference in the effectiveness of using EFT is the user's ability to contact the problem.

We have so many thoughts, all of which are linked to our body via our general neurology; so many memories; so many stored experiences. These stored experiences all have the patterns of how the meridians were flowing at the time stored with them, too; and certain thought patterns direct how the meridians are functioning from second to second in a dynamic, interlinked system.

To direct the tapping to the required area, we focus the mind on the problem by using a statement of the problem: "I am afraid of heights."

Preferably, this is spoken out loud to engage as much of the neurology as possible and to contact the problem as directly as possible.

It is important to note at this point that the statement is NOT to be confused with an affirmation (see also EFT & Affirmations in the A-Z of EFT).

Oftentimes, it is only a small part of the unconscious mind that holds certain fears, angers, sadnesses and griefs - the person KNOWS on the conscious level that they are a child of the universe, for example, but there are parts of them which don't agree and think they're a bad person. It is those parts that require the healing and balancing that EFT has to offer, and these are spoken to directly by allowing them for once the honest truth of the matter - the opening statement is like the key that unlocks the dungeon they've been hiding in for so long.

Here are a couple of stories to illustrate this point.

I gave a demonstration of EFT for a Weight Watchers group. One lady there tried it with the opening statement of, "I'm not as thin as I would like to be" and said that she really felt nothing when she tapped.

I asked her gently to think for a moment if that was really what she thought when she looked in the mirror, and she shook her head and whispered, "No, I think I'm a fat pig."

When she tapped using that statement, the shift was extreme and the release visible to all and joyful in its intensity. She has since told me that this moment constituted a true turning point in her life.

Another lady who was pregnant and afraid of giving birth, used the statement, "I am apprehensive of the forthcoming event." Again, nothing happened.

I asked her to go within and try and find a better description that would ring more true to her and she came up with, "I'm scared to death of giving birth".

Tapping on this provided her with the release she so desperately needed, cured her backache and headache on the spot, and allowed her to continue forward with her pregnancy without further problems.

In a moment, take a little time to think about a problem that you have, a pain, a fear, an illness or perhaps a phobia, something that always makes you depressed when you think about it, just generally any negative emotion you are happy to release now and forever.

- Choose a statement that rings true to you, choosing words that make sense to you and you alone. **The more forthright, direct and truthful you can be, the more profound a change you will experience.**

Statements for Physical Ailments & Pain

Opening statements for physical ailments can be created in many ways.

If there is a physical symptom connected with your illness, you probably have already a way you describe it routinely to others; use this for your opening statement.

- I've got that tightness in my neck again;
- My back's killing me;
- That churning in my stomach;
- This ringing in my ears, etc.

You can just **name your illness** - my hay fever, my psoriasis, my allergy, this darned migraine.

A very powerful help for physical illness is to **focus on your feelings about** the illness, too:

- I hate this back ache;
- This (condition) is killing me;
- This (condition) is destroying my life;
- This (condition) is driving me to desperation; etc.

Remember the main important part of the directional opening statements is that you know what you're talking about, and that what you're saying makes perfect sense to you.

c. The Set Up

Now that we've named the problem, we can start with the **Set Up** which consists of

- rubbing (stimulating) the sore spot
- and making the first opening statement

which directs the treatment to the right place in your mind/body totality.

For the opening statement, we use the following routine:

Find the sore spot on either side of your chest; rub it round gently and say:

> **"Even though I (insert problem statement),**
> **I deeply and profoundly accept myself."**

For example, if you decided your problem was "My back is killing me", you would say as your Set Up Statement:

> **"Even though my back is killing me,**
> **I deeply and profoundly accept myself."**

Repeat this three times, rubbing the Sore Spot continuously as you do so, and please do endeavour to put some meaning and energy into the "I deeply and profoundly accept myself" part.

You don't have to say those exact words. You could say:

- I love myself,
- I deeply and completely accept myself;
- God loves me;
- I am willing to heal now;

… or any variation that carries this kind of meaning for you; you can also leave the acceptance statement out altogether if it makes you feel unhappy or uncomfortable and simply do the Set Up with stimulating the Sore Sport and stating the nature of the problem.

I have known a few clients who could not bring a statement of acceptance of themselves over their lips at all and we began the sessions with tapping for "Even though I don't accept myself at all, I deeply and profoundly accept myself!"

When working with young children, you can use a version that makes sense to their age group, such as "Even though (problem),

- I'm a great kid;
- I really like myself;
- My mummy loves me totally;
- I'm always OK;

… or any variation that has a positive meaning, is acceptable and makes sense.

d. The Round

Following the Set Up, we now tap all the points, starting from the top (Eyebrow) and ending up with the Karate Chop Point on the hand.

As you tap each point, repeat a shortened version of the Set Up Statement which is called the reminder phrase; so if your set up statement was,

"Even though I hate and despise my boss,
I deeply and profoundly love and accept myself",

… you say the **reminder (shortened version) phrase:**

"I hate and despise my boss"

… on each point at the same time as you tap.

The reason for repeating the reminder statement is that we can get distracted very easily; by repeating the statement on each point we stop ourselves from thinking about lunch, the next appointment or how the weather has changed and make sure the tapping goes directly to the problem you're working on.

Once you know where the points are, the round of tapping (excluding the set up) should take no more than about 2 minutes, unless you feel a strong urge to stay longer on one particular point which can sometimes happen.

e. The 9 Gamut

This is the middle part in what is sometimes called the EFT sandwich:

Following tapping all the points about 7 times from the top of the eyebrow to the karate chop point, you tap continuously on the Gamut point, and then do the following:

28

- move your eyes from the floor to the ceiling without moving your head, trying to keep the tracking smooth, and back again.

- move your eyes from left to right and back again

- move your eyes in a big circle and back again

- hum - Happy Birthday To You (or another tune or just a scale) for about one bar;

- count - one two three four five

- hum again

Take a deep breath in and out.

As you do these (at first slightly unusual) things*, repeat the statement in between as best you can to keep yourself focused on the problem in hand.

Then, repeat the Round one more time, tapping all the points from the eyebrow to the karate chop point. Take a deep breath and allow yourself a moment to reflect on how you feel now, making a note of what has changed.

* Note: The eye movements are linked to various brain functions and the reason for the humming-counting-humming manoeuvre is to switch between hemispheres quite quickly; both are designed to "wake up" your neurology so the tapping can go to work on the problem.

It is for this reason that more advanced users sometimes do without the 9 Gamut part as it isn't always necessary to "wake up the brain" to get the changes; to begin with, I recommend you do it every time until you are completely familiar with the technique and have acquired a "feel" for when it is necessary and when it isn't.

If you leave out the 9 Gamut treatment, remember to tap the Gamut point by itself because it is a very important part of your meridian system.

f. Testing Your Changes

A great way to ascertain from yourself or others just how you feel is to put a number on it. The technical term is taking a SUDs Level or SUDs Scale reading, which stands for Subjective Units of Disturbance.

What that means is you ask yourself:

On a scale of 10 to 0, 10 being the highest imaginable pain/ upset/ distress/ fear/ sadness/ discomfort, and 0 being completely calm, pain free, tranquil, relaxed and happy, how would you rate what you are experiencing at this moment?

This works for emotions as well as for physical sensations and even for beliefs which might be a problem:

On a scale of ten to zero:

- how depressed are you right now?
- how painful is your leg?
- how bad is your fear of heights?
- how distressing is this memory?
- how much do you hate this person?

Before you begin tapping for any subject or problem, take the time to take a SUDS rating and make a mental note of it. Then, when you have completed a Sandwich treatment, ask the question again to find how much has changed. It's a good way to be able to assess how well the treatment has worked and if you need to repeat the treatment.

Sometimes, the problem can go from as high as 10 to as low as 0 in a single Sandwich treatment.

More often though, you start with 8 or 9, and after a round of tapping, the severity is reduced to a 4 or a 5.

This means that the treatment is beginning to work but there's more to be done.

Testing is a **very important** part of the EFT technique overall; see also Testing in the A-Z, Part 2.

g. Subsequent Treatment Rounds

If the original set up statement was something along the lines of, "Even though I have this problem", you have tapped a first round on "this problem", and upon checking with yourself, this problem is not as severe anymore but still noticeable, change the Opening Statement to:

"Even though there is still some of this problem remaining",

or

"Even though I still have some of this problem".

When you're down to a rating of "Oh its a tiny little bit now" which would be a 2, 1 or a half on the subjective rating scale, a third round can be done with the opening statement of,

**"I want to completely overcome this problem now
and I fully and completely accept myself".**

And that's it!

EFT is as simple as that.

There's no need for you to worry about getting it wrong, or getting the wrong statement.

ALL TAPPING YOU DO IS GOOD FOR YOU.

Any tapping you do stimulates the meridians, relaxes you, calms you and makes you feel a little better, even if you get totally the wrong opening affirmation and the original problem has not yet shifted.

31

Just try again with a different start up phrase, or think about what the truth about the problem might be.

One thing I have found particularly helpful is to ask your friends what they think you should say!

This will crop up again in various other sections, but it really has been my experience that our own neurology blindsides us sometimes, and especially on issues we have been working on for many years. The one thing you're probably not thinking of and which would make the "bull's eye" opening statement is the one thing which is blatantly obvious to everyone else.

This is not a character defect, but simply a fact of life.

So relax, enjoy and here's a short Trouble Shooting section on the most commonly asked questions:

h. Frequently Asked Questions

I'm not sure I have found the exact right points?
Don't worry about that. As you tap, the vibrations spread out through your skin and bones and can be felt for quite a distance. As long as you're roughly in the right area, it will work. To try this for yourself, tap the Under Eye point now and notice how far and wide you can feel the reverberations.

I can't find the Sore Spot?
If you can't find the Sore Spot, and this can sometimes happen according to the type of problem you're working on, just place your whole flat hand over the general area, much the same gesture as though you were taking an oath of allegiance.

Wait until you can feel the warmth of your hand on your skin through your clothes, and rub the whole hand round instead.

This, by the way, can also be very soothing in and of itself in a moment of crisis.

I'm really unsure what to say for the opening statement?
A whole EFT Sandwich takes only about 4 minutes altogether. So it's not a matter of life or death to get a good resonant statement first time round.

If you're very pressed for time, you could get a piece of paper and brain storm some variations first, then pick the ones that "feel" the most intense when you read them out aloud. Also, speaking is not actually always necessary to contact a problem. Wait until you have read the sections on memory, emotions and substances, there are many more ideas of how you can contact the problem successfully.

Do I always have to do the whole Sandwich?
No, not necessarily. After the first round, and before you get to the 9 Gamut treatment, you can stop and take a SUDs level reading.

If there has been a lot of relief to the problem, you can go right away to starting again with the "Even though there is still some of this problem remaining" version; if it's really low, you can go straight to "I want to overcome this problem completely".

However, for the first week or so of using EFT I would advise you to do the full Sandwich for every problem, just to make sure you really get the hang of it.

Which side of the face/body should I tap with which hand?
The bilateral meridians run in tandem so changes in one affects changes in another.

Therefore you can please yourself and tap as comes most naturally or is the most comfortable with either hand on either side.

I've missed a point!
Relax. The main thing is, did you get a good noticeable shift? That's all that matters. It only takes a few goes and you are completely familiar with the procedure.

How hard/fast should I tap?
You should tap with light, short movements that resonate just like you would tap on a drum to make it ring out.

Don't tap too hard – it should not hurt in any way, but you should be able to feel it clearly and also feel the resonance in your body.

As to speed, try different speeds and rhythms to find something that feels right for the problem you are currently working on. *See also Rhythm & Percussion in the Addendum.*

Nothing's happening! I'm doing it all wrong!
Please, be calm! This is a gentle and very easy treatment procedure.

It is very forgiving to inaccuracies and truly foolproof.

If you have read the instructions and looked on the chart to the locations of the points, chances are you ARE doing it right. If the Earth didn't move for you on your first attempt, try a different opening statement, or a different subject or topic. Play with it. Experiment.

Allow yourself time to experience how the treatment affected you right after you did it, a few hours after that, the next day and so on. Share it with a friend and try it on each other. Read the rest of the book, there are many, many more ideas and suggestions to come.

But most of all, "Keep At It!".

I find it difficult/impossible to contact any emotions at all.
This is a problem you share with about 15% of the population, so it's not that uncommon. Think about the problem and do the tapping anyway. Be persistent. Also, read the section on "Fail Safes" in Part V very carefully. If still nothing happens, have a session with an experienced practitioner to "unlock your system".

I've tapped on something small and now I've unlocked a whole hornet's nest of terrible feelings and memories!
If you are truly overwhelmed by negative emotions, you need to speak with a Meridian Therapist.

What can help tremendously in moments of overwhelm on your own is to tap without any opening statements to let the relaxation go where it is most needed, or to do very general statements such as, "Even though I can't cope …", "Even though I'm overwhelmed …" etc. and to leave any specific or serious traumas until you can speak with a practitioner.

How often can I use EFT?
If you are someone who is very anxious to make many changes fast, or you have an obsess ional streak to your character, **take it easy** with the frequency of EFT treatments.

I refer to working on any one particular issue to it's conclusion as "a session" – this may take a single round, sometimes it takes many rounds as the deep reasons for the problem begin to unfold. Personally, I would say that two "sessions" per day are more than enough when you are working on very serious issues, such as traumatic war-, rape- or abuse memories.

You can use EFT much more often than that for simply eliminating cravings or pains that come along frequently. If you are working on one particular issue that is very important to you, you can tap for this up to five times a day; and of course, in emergency situations you can always use EFT again as and when you have to. You can also use EFT as a general relaxation and de-stressing method by tapping a round first thing in the morning or last thing at night, without making a particular Opening Statement and just for the re-balancing effect.

When you begin to use EFT, you will note the difference between a "session" of tapping and "general tapping" to alleviate something, reduce something or relax; if you have had a real breakthrough "session" with EFT on a major topic, I would highly recommend that you give yourself and all your systems a time to come into balance with the new order of being before starting on the next issue.

The Safety Note Repeated:

Emotional Freedom Techniques are a wonderful self help tool BUT: EFT is powerful and makes changes to your body and to your thoughts. We therefore recommend strongly that anyone suffering from diagnosed psychiatric disorders, takes psychoactive medication or is under ongoing treatment with a counsellor, psychologist, psychiatrist, outpatient department **should ALWAYS consult with their care providers** before starting any new form of treatment, including EFT Emotional Freedom Techniques. **If in any doubt, stop and seek advice from your care provider or an experienced MET (meridian energy therapies) professional.**

i. Side Effects

EFT is in my opinion and experience completely safe. There are some physical things that happen frequently when you start to apply EFT routinely. You might or might not experience some, any, all or none of these; here is a list of physical effects I have observed:

- **Sleepiness**

I have noted that many people vibrate with tension as a matter of course and regardless of whether they are working, playing or resting. I used to be amongst them!

When fears especially are addressed with EFT, this anxiety leaves and the person in question starts to relax in ways they might not have experienced for many years.

One of the first symptoms of this is an unusual amount of yawning during or after the treatment, and a desire to sleep. One of my telephone clients would virtually fall asleep in the middle of the session and I had to shout at her to wake her up enough to finish the treatment! This only lasts for a period of a week or two, until the body has recovered and become used to the new levels of working freely and without the added stressed out anxiety.

36

- **Tearing Of The Eyes**

Not to be confused with crying triggered by high emotion, this tearing of the eyes is a symptom directly linked to increased levels of certain naturally occurring brain chemicals (which have been noted to be present during states of enhanced brain activity and enlightenment experiences).

I note this particular symptom with much joy when it appears in myself or in my clients; it's a physical sign that some very profound deep level shifts are taking place.

- **"Dreamy" Feeling**

Many clients report a feeling of haziness around their thinking for a minute or two just after a treatment round; after a "heavy session", it can last for longer.

This is a sign that there's a lot of activity going on within their minds and bodies as new neurological pathways are being created and old ones are being re-routed. Until normal functioning is re-established, one should rest and not undertake any challenging activities. Drinking water and gentle exercise can help speed the process but it is a natural occurrence that takes its own course and is a necessary part of the healing that is taking place.

- **"Body Noises"**

As the body relaxes during tapping, you might find various body noises such as a grumbling stomach, burping etc. It only happens sometimes, but once again, greet these obvious signs of relaxation and relief with joy - whatever you're doing, it's having a highly beneficial effect on your system.

I can't repeat this enough – "tapping" is good for you.

It's always relaxing and calming, so even if you don't have at this present time a problem you need help with, start doing a round or two at a convenient time a day for nothing much in particular, and a round before you go to bed.

Make a note of what benefits it brings to you, and when the time comes and you find you wish to apply it on a real problem, you're practised and ready to reap the rewards.

j. Long Term Tapping

I often hear that people say,

"When I first used it, my (hay fever/migraine/pain/fear of public speaking/height phobia/ desire for heroin/etc) just went away. But two days later, it came back ..."

Some people then go on to proclaim that the treatment didn't work.

This really makes my head spin. That's like saying, "I got this plate, I washed it up, and then was clean again. But today I've eaten off it and now it's dirty once more - and I have concluded that washing up doesn't work!"

If you can tap any problem away, that really does mean that the treatment has worked.

If it comes back, I would suggest that it might be that it would be wise to repeat the treatment to get the benefit again.

k. Repeat Treatments

Repeat treatments are necessary when:

- **The root cause hasn't yet been found and eliminated.**

In some cases, it really is necessary to find a sympathetic practitioner to help discover what needs to be done to overcome the problem once and for all.

With very deep issues and especially, issues of self identity (i.e. if this problem was resolved, the person in question feels they wouldn't be the same person anymore at all), get some outside assistance. In these cases, two heads are simply much better than one, plus having someone walk beside you for moral support is useful in any circumstance.

In other cases, it is possible that by varying the opening statements and continued tapping, you will get to the root cause eventually all by yourself.

- **There are undiscovered ASPECTS to the problem.**

Let's say, there's this man who wants to use EFT to overcome his money problems. So he taps away on all kinds of things that could be connected, and it's getting much better but is still not completely resolved. Then one day, he visits his parents and realises with a flash of insight that if he were successful, he would somehow make all his father's hard work seem like such a waste of time.

"Being disloyal" to the father was the one aspect he had overlooked, it had never occurred to him.

Another and far more simple example is that of the woman who is afraid of spiders. She taps for it and feels ok, then goes to the pet shop to view a real life spider.

There is no fear - until the spider starts scurrying around in the cage, at which point the fear returns.

What happened there was that she had cured the fear of "still spiders" - but there had been another undiscovered aspect, i.e. the fear of "running spiders" which was a different proposition altogether.

When she tapped on that fear, the whole spider problem resolved itself and she could hold the spider in her hand and have it walk up her arm.

- **The Force Of Habit**

If a problem has existed for a very long time, it's just become habitual. The tapping re-aligns the meridians to flow freely and positively, but they may bounce back if there's stress or other environmental influences into the old and more familiar pattern.

All you need to do in this case is to repeat the treatment for a few days until your meridians have become used to the new order of things.

- **Environmental Toxins**

In a very few cases, there are some environmental toxins present that may influence how effectively the treatments last. This is very rare however, and the above three reasons are far more likely to be causing the need for repeated applications.

Look on the bright side. How many repeat applications of aspirin have you applied to yourself in the course of your life? And did you ever demand for just one moment that one application would cure you of headaches forever?

I just thought I put the efficiency of EFT into perspective by this example. Of course we expect of the treatment that it cure the problem once and for all, because it usually does.

If your symptoms come creeping back, tap some more; the best advice is, "Keep At It!".

5. Psychological Reversal

(or, how to heave a deep, great sigh of relief at not having to struggle along on will power any more!)

For me, one of the most wonderful ideas in the meridian therapies is the concept of psychological reversal.

There's much debate amongst the experts as to what's going on, but it seems that shock, trauma, and most of all, FEAR, can cause the energy flow relating to a particular subject to become reversed. This process is sometimes likened to batteries having been placed accidentally upside down; when you come to switch it on, the radio simply cannot work.

For example, most people have one or more, or a single massive reversal on health related issues.

If they were muscle tested, they would test weak on "I want to be healthy" which means they don't believe it, and for them, that it isn't actually true at all - the Psychological Reversal makes the opposite happen to what they want to have happen.

In cases of chronic illness that seems resistant to any kind of holistic or allopathic treatment, or where after each kind of treatment, the symptoms subside for a little while, and then come back with a vengeance, Psychological Reversal is almost certainly at the root of the problem.

I find the concept of Psychological Reversal particularly poignant when applied to people who have tried many times to make a positive shift in their lives and somehow, always seem to end up right back where they started.

These are the people who struggle endlessly with substance addictions, weight- and fitness problems and the like. These are the people who are trying to fight themselves using "will power" to overcome their own internal programming that runs to the reverse of what everyone - including parts of themselves - are telling them they "should" or "should not" be doing.

The problem with using will power when there is psychological reversal is this: **will power was never meant for long-term use.** It was designed originally to allow the mind to override the body, briefly, in moments of emergency and necessity, such as being able to run into a burning house to save a child, or to override fear in order to face fighting a lion.

Using will power, therefore, to try and overcome problems and force oneself to be doing certain things on a long-term basis has two possible outcomes, both of which are problematic to say the least.

One outcome would be to succeed, and to continuously override the parts that are reversed. This continuous exertion of will power drains the system and the body of energy, creates rigidity in mind and body and can have serious repercussions for long term health - the conflict doesn't go away, it may just go underground and express in all kinds of mental, psychological and physical dis-eases instead.

The other outcome is that the one who is trying to override a psychological reversal with will power simply can't keep it up. As we've mentioned above, "running on will power" drains enormous amounts of energy from the system, and if there are other demands on this energy such as outside stress, or low energy states such as feeling down or depressed one day, feeling a little ill, picking up a bug, that's all that's needed for the will power to collapse and the reversed parts to take over once more - that's the "recovering alcoholic" in a moment of crisis who turns to the bottle, or the fat lady who's had some bad news and makes straight for the fridge.

The long-term effects of this are a terrible toll on the persons self esteem. Every time this happens, they are the first to berate themselves viciously for being weak, useless, hopeless and for "having no will power". Many therapists too, spoken or unspoken, tend to share societies view that people who can't control themselves are somehow weak, less worthy, that they're not trying hard enough, or that they want to suffer.

Energy reversal takes all that emotional blackmail out of the process.

Treatment Points For Psychological Energy Reversal

Treating for energy reversal is easy and profoundly effective - there are two specific points that correct a reversal within seconds, namely

- **the Sore Spot**, and

- **the Karate Chop** point.

Together with EFTs excellence at uncovering root causes, and helping to build true self esteem, no matter what presenting problems there are in a person's life, here now there is a technique available to take pain and suffering out of long standing problems that have caused intense pain and terrible internal battles for so many.

Even long standing psychological reversals can be re-reversed and habitual patterns undone; and best of all, as Gary Craig says, "It's not a character flaw, it's just something that happened", finally taking the burden of guilt and shame from those afflicted by nothing more, or nothing less, than a simple psychological reversal. (see also: EFT & Willpower in the A-Z).

6. This Is Just Too Simple!

At this point, some people get a confused look in their eye and cry out, "This is it? This is all there is? Tapping just a few points and saying those statements? Surely something as simple as this can't possibly be of any use with serious problems such as fear of death, bereavement, depression and panic attacks?"

To answer this, it is important to remember that the whole treatment is based on the theory of the intervening step between experiencing something as a negative emotion, a physical sensation or both, and the trigger in thought, memory or in the environment.

Here is the central discovery of meridian energy therapies once more:

A Thought or Memory

⬇

Triggers

⬇

A Disruption In the Body's Energy System

⬇

Which is experienced as:

⬇

Physical or Psychological Pain

This intervening step is the way the meridians transfer subtle energy around the whole mind/body system. It is indeed a simple theory, but as you will find out, it works in practise – the ultimate test for any theory. And, of course, often the most surprising and elegant solutions are the most straightforward ones.

So now, and for your convenience, here is a single EFT treatment all the way through for easy reference.

7. EFT - The Whole Treatment At A Glance

Step 1 - Name the problem, clearly, directly and truthfully.

Step 2 - Take a SUDs reading of how bad it is right now 0-10

Step 3 - Do the Set Up - "Even though I have this problem, I deeply and profoundly accept myself" three times out loud, whilst rubbing the Sore Spot or tapping on the Karate Chop point to correct for any possible Psychological Reversal.

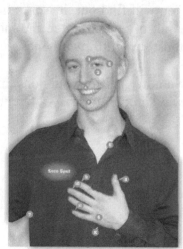

Step 4 - Choose a shortened "reminder phrase" and say this on each point as you tap from the top of the eyebrow to the karate chop point.

Step 5 - Do the 9 Gamut procedure (eyes left to right, up to down, in a circle, hum/count/hum) whilst tapping or holding the Gamut point.

Step 6 - Do another round with the reminder phrase as in Step 4.

Step 7 - Take a deep breath in and out and take a new SUDs reading.

Subsequent Rounds - Change the Set Up to:

> **Even though there is still some of this problem remaining, I deeply and profoundly accept myself.**

… and finally to:

> **I want to get completely over this problem and I deeply and profoundly accept myself.**

… to get your problem right down to 0.

Congratulations! You have learned how to do EFT!

Part II - EFT & Memories

I have a notion that most everything that troubles us in our daily lives is the result of limiting beliefs about the world and ourselves, and these limiting beliefs were formed as the result of traumatic memories.

I came to this conclusion doing many years of what is called pinpoint hypnotherapy.

The idea behind this is that if you have problem now but if there was ever a time in your life, even just after birth, when you did not have the problem, it must mean by definition that something must have happened to cause you to have acquired the problem.

To give an example, a pre-EFT hypnosis client of mine who suffered from hay fever since he was 6 years old (but did not suffer from it before he was six years old), was stung by a bee whilst rolling down a grassy slope covered in freshly cut hay.

He had a shock reaction and nearly died; his immune system concluded that there was some kind of link between being seriously ill and the freshly cut hay and so the hay fever was born. Once this link was undone, hay fever became a thing of the past where it so rightfully belonged.

To undo this link, although of course it is possible, is a bit of a feat in hypnotherapy; with EFT, it's easy as pie.

The discovery statement says that what causes the problem is not the memory in and of itself, but the way the memory triggers a disruption in the body's energy system. This disruption is stored infinitely, just as the memory itself, and will re-play itself, just like the memory, when triggered.

In the case of our hay fever man, what caused the extreme reaction in his immune system was the red alert transmitted through the meridians each time a whiff of vegetation in bloom came his way; once the red alert was

47

tapped into smooth flowing, the immune system no longer had to respond by becoming hyperactive.

You can use EFT with memories in many ways, but before we get to that, let me tell you what happens when you treat emotions with EFT so you know what to expect when you begin to work with memories of your own.

1. Removing Emotions From Memories

Common Questions Answered

What happens when you tap on memories and experiences from the past?

The memory remains intact.
Or, in other words, once the emotional charge has been taken from a memory using EFT, it's still there, still accessible, and often becomes far clearer as a result - people report all kinds of new insights once their minds are no longer clouded by the terrible disturbances from the emotions.

The memory (and the subject matter connected to the memory) becomes accessible to common sense.
All manner of decisions, many of them quite irrational, are usually the result of traumatic memories. A woman who had a particularly bad experience with one man, for example, might end up with a belief that ALL men are unsafe to be with. Logic tells us that this isn't reasonable or rational, but the emotion behind this belief makes it un-contradictable to the owner of the memory.

Once the emotional charge has been removed, common sense can kick in and the woman in question will be able to make a rational distinction, not only to the understanding that there definitely are some very unsavoury men out there and that steps must be taken to identify them, avoid them if possible, protect oneself from them; but also, that there are definitely nice and good men too.

Emotions Do NOT Protect Us
Many times I hear the objection that if a particular fear is removed, the person feels they wouldn't be safe in a particular situation. For example, if you lived in an area where poisonous spiders are at large and you overcame your spider phobia, you would be more at risk.

This is absolutely not so. A freaked out, panic stricken individual is in no position to take control of their own safety, or plan carefully how to avoid danger to life and limb. On the contrary, it is the panic stricken

49

individual who makes the fatal mistake - running headlong into a blind alley, stumbling and slipping on the cliff side, reeling wildly backwards from one spider and falling onto another.

If this should come up for you, remember it is not the negative emotion that protects you, it is your common sense that does, and that will protect you far better if you can keep your head, your body and your mind sharp, clear, focussed and alert.

Negative emotions were sent to "teach us things"
This is a consideration for some, and all we need say about that is, "Thank you, the lesson is well and truly learned".

Remember that all the learnings you have had as a result of whatever has happened will remain completely intact in all ways, and that you will have even more learnings once the emotional charge has been taken away or reduced to bearable levels.

To give an example, one of my clients had had a very unfortunate "first contact" sexual experience with another virgin; it was all terribly embarrassing, painful in many more ways than just emotionally, and altogether the kind of thing that can turn a girl off enjoying any kind of sexual endeavour for a very long time indeed. Once the negative emotions had been released, she smiled and giggled and commented on how terrible it must have been for the boy involved; she then fell thoughtful as she contemplated all kinds of insights that now began to reveal themselves to her for the first time.

Negative emotions are "just" punishment
In some cases, people use negative emotions as a form of self punishment for all manner of things they did wrong, or thought wrong, or thought they did wrong.

Anger, or even rage, at the self, is probably the most destructive amongst all emotional forces; yet they exist in many ways, and not only amongst people who were sexually abused as children.

A fellow therapist tells the story of a man who was partially responsible for an industrial accident which poisoned himself and a number of

50

colleagues; this was seven years ago and everyone else had healed and moved on with their lives, but his symptoms continued to persist. During a tapping session, it was revealed that the man carried an inordinate amount of anger at himself for "having been so stupid" as to let the accident happen; this anger demanded he should continue to suffer and was not allowed to ever get any better. Once the negative emotions were released, his injuries, finally, began to heal.

Then there is also the perverse human response of, "They've hurt me. Now I'll suffer even more, that'll show 'em!", as exemplified by the jilted lover who goes about making himself as unhappy as possible, in a strange attempt to punish the other (who, generally, really doesn't care!).

Another variation on this theme are people who hold on to grievances and won't allow themselves to heal, because in some way this would justify what a perpetrator did to them.

Although I understand what this position feels like, having held it myself on a number of issues and occasions, I really don't think it's fair or right that someone who is already suffering, should have to suffer even more to make a point.

If you suspect you might suffer from a similar misunderstanding, you might like to begin by tapping for statements like, "Even though I still haven't suffered enough ..." or, "Even though I cannot forgive ..." as a starting point to being allowed to heal.

Suffering Is Noble Or Necessary
Especially on the subject of bereavement, it often comes up that the owner of the negative emotions feels they need to hold on to the pain to show how much the deceased meant to them - a kind of emotional "climbing onto the bonfire with the body".

There are two things about that. Firstly, love never demands or rejoices in suffering.

If I died, I would be heartbroken to think that my children or friends made their lives a misery because of me in any way. I would want them to be happy and I can only guess this surely must be so with others who love as I do, too.

The other thing is that you are totally in charge of what you want to do with your emotions - you do not have to tap any issue down to a 0 if you don't want to (see also Bereavement in the A-Z).

With some issues, it can be better to reduce the level of pain over time to give your systems a chance to adjust.

I call this:

2. The Stepping Stone Approach

Let's imagine, for a moment, that there's this person who is agoraphobic. She is married, had the problem for about 20 years, and not only her own life but the entire household including husband, children, aged parents and all the friends are adjusted to living around, through and with the problem.

For her to all of a sudden jump off the couch and start engaging in out-of-doors activities would probably cause havoc on all kinds of levels. This need not necessarily be so, by the way, but this is often the reason that there is sincere resistance to overcoming problems that have been very much a part of a person's life and have shaped that person's life and all their interactions for a long time.

A very safe way of dealing with this is to reduce the problem a step at a time over a period of time.

This "stepping stone" approach has the following advantages:

1. It gives not only the person themselves but also their surroundings and the people in their lives time to adjust, to discover new behaviours and ways of proceeding and relating;
2. It makes it more likely that the person will want to undertake the change in the first place, as this approach is more gentle and supportive;
3. As the change is less rapid, it is also less fearful;
4. Other issues that play a part in the problem can be resolved one at a time along the way in a holistic, cohesive and most importantly, completely ecological fashion.

3. Treating Meanings Rather Than Treating Emotions Or Memories

Some people truly do not want to treat or "tap away" certain emotions or the emotions that were experienced during certain events. There is a sense that it these emotions are important or even vital in some way, and if you should come across this, rather than to argue with a client or yourself, there is an alternative approach that helps relieve the symptoms just as well.

Instead of the emotions or the past events directly, you tap on "the meanings" that were made from the events that happened. For example, someone who was attacked whilst walking home and very traumatised and shocked in the cause of this, might have made meanings of these events as follows:

- "I can't protect myself."
- "You can never know when disaster strikes – it could be any second, any time."
- "People are out to get me."
- "I am not safe ever, anywhere."

These kinds of "meanings" from the events are a big problem, and unlike the events themselves are rarely protected by objections that makes someone hesitate or not want to treat this because we are well aware that although it's completely understandable to have come to such conclusions, they are not and never the "whole story". Consciously and rationally, we already know that well enough and it is usually a huge relief to be able to lay these "false meanings" to rest, once and for all.

Now, having cleared the way, we can take a look at how you can use EFT with specific memories or issues resulting from them.

4. How To Use EFT With Memories

a. The Statement Approach

Generally, this is the most commonly used and most commonly useful way to overcome problems of any kind. Simply name the problem in question, such as,

- **I can't make money**
- **My wife drives me insane**
- **I have this shoulder pain**
- **I'm so afraid to die**
- **God doesn't like me**
- **I'll never learn to (…)**
- **I'm useless at (…)**
- **People hate me**
- **I have this wart on my nose**
- **I'm terrified of snakes**
- **I'm terribly constipated**
- **My child is failing at school**
- **My mother never loved me**
- **I can't live without cocaine**
- **I have no talent for ESP**
- **My body disgusts me**

Put this into the opening statement surrounded by, "Even though …, I deeply and profoundly accept myself" or any phrasing that makes sense to you or the person you are working with.

This is the easiest and most straightforward way of applying EFT; it doesn't demand any intuitive skills, languaging skills, investigative skills or therapeutic skills at all and is very effective indeed.

Usually, during and after the round, as the original stuck problem is beginning to soften, dissolve and move, new opening statements become apparent quite naturally.

These could be other "aspects" of the same problem or related memories, thoughts and ideas as well as meanings that are coming to light.

Simply continue to tap on what presents itself until a resolution has been reached or you feel that it is time to stop.

b. The Keyword Approach

Some issues/memories are such that you simply cannot talk about them because as soon as you try to do so, you are overwhelmed with emotions.

In this case, think of a single keyword which represents the totality of the issue/memory to you and start with, "Even though I have this Rose memory, I deeply and profoundly accept myself", for example, inserting your own key word into the opening statement and the reminder phrase.

You might never have to say anything else but that keyword and heal the entire issue/memory; in some other cases, different aspects become apparent and you can choose new keywords to represent these.

This approach, by the way, is also excellent for addressing emotions you cannot put a name or reason to.

I had a strange emotional reaction to a song once, feeling like crying every time the line appeared: "and the sky so blue" in the chorus. To this day I have no idea what caused this or what it was all about; I tapped for "Even though I have this "sky so blue" sadness ..." and it released the emotion, quite without any need for cognition, investigation or further trouble.

If this is still too much to cope with, you can abbreviate it even further and give a short key word and just tap for "blue" instead; the more distant the keyword (or you could use a colour, a number, or any form of symbol at all) the more control you have. After tapping with the keyword for a while, you might find that the emotional intensity has been reduced sufficiently so you can begin to work with the subject/memory more directly.

Sometimes the keyword approach works all by itself and you find that the associated memory/subject feels neutral when you come to check; at other times, you can go on to more direct opening statements once some of the overwhelm of emotions has been reduced with the keyword approach – the key has opened the whole topic to be healed, step by step.

c. The Story Approach

This is a very useful way of dealing with memories that you might have worked with for a long time, in counselling or elsewhere, and that are still not completely resolved.

You can do this either by yourself or with another, but make sure you speak the story of the memory out loud.

There are good neurological reasons for this; brain activity is far more comprehensive when someone speaks about something they remember out loud, as opposed to thinking about it silently.

Start at the beginning, and tell the story of what happened as though you were telling someone you trusted deeply.

Monitor yourself carefully for:

- any quavering in your voice,
- voice changing in tone, pitch, volume from your normal way of conversational speech;
- any shuddering breaths,
- short breath,
- physical sensations such as a tightness in the chest, lump in the throat etc;
- emotion welling up as you say certain words.

As soon as you notice anything like this, stop and tap on the last phrase you said.

When you feel that this phrase and what it represents has been resolved, start your story again from the beginning to make sure that you can get past the "sticking point" easily this time. Then, continue with the rest of the story, stopping every time to tap whenever you suspect there is a charge behind your words, until you can tell the whole story and it's perfectly calm from beginning to end.

Here's an example of this which happened with a real person on the telephone:

Telephone Session Story Approach Example

Client: "I had been shopping and I came home. As usual, I flicked on the telephone answering machine because it was flashing. And there was this message saying my mother had died." *(Client takes deep shuddering breath, last part of the sentence her voice was breaking)*

- (We tapped for: **Even though this message said that my mother had died**).

Client continues: "I got the message that my mother had died *(no change in voice after the round of EFT, calm breathing)* and I just didn't know what to do, I was in such a daze. *(shallow erratic breathing again, voice very unsteady).*

- (We tapped for: **Even though I didn't know what to do**, and **Even though I was in such a daze**)

Client continues: "I was in such a daze, I just climbed into the car and started driving. It was a terrible journey, I cried and cried all the way."

- (We tapped for, **Even though it was a terrible journey**, (which brought up an aspect of, **Even though I thought I would have an accident**; and, **Even though I thought I would never get there**) and, **Even though I cried and cried all the way**)

58

Client continues: "When finally I got there, I was so exhausted; I thought I was going to die as well."

- (We tapped for, **Even though I was so exhausted**, and **Even though I thought I was going to die as well**)

After this last statement – "Even though I thought I was going to die as well." the client took a deep, deep sigh and said, "I feel completely different now, as though a huge weight has been lifted."

I asked her to tell me the story one more time, and this time she told it without hesitation or any changes in voice, bearing, breathing or any other indications of emotional upset.

I was satisfied that this particular memory was now healed, and she was extremely relieved, happy, smiling and told me she felt lighter and younger than she had for years.

Her driving phobia duly disappeared and so did her migraine attacks.

The Story approach to using EFT is a very thorough method for cleaning and healing memories; as a side note to therapists, this approach also brings up "missing pieces" in memories, i.e. points of complete dis-association.

These can be opened up with such statements as, "Even though I don't know what happened when I came around the corner" or, "Even though I can't remember how I got home" etc. and then released as usual.

d. The Picture Release

An interesting way of directing the balancing effects of EFT towards the right areas without having to say anything at all is to use a photograph or any other picture that represents an issue in it's totality.

- One lady re-discovered previously forgotten positive memories and happy aspects of her childhood by tapping whilst looking at photographs of her younger self;

- A gentleman used a photograph of his ex-wife to release intense feelings of anger, sadness and betrayal that he could not put into words.

- An older lady who had many issues to do with ethnic cleansing and a whole host of traumatic memories from her early childhood used a picture in a newspaper to begin the release of the issue;

- I've recently heard of a lady using a television programme about aerial photography to clear her fear of heights successfully in real life.

One very interesting application I heard about recently was a gentleman who hated looking at photographs of himself. He rightfully concluded that this was the symptom of a deep seated problem relating to self esteem and spent a month holding photographs of himself at various stages in his life, looking into his own eyes and tapping without speaking. He told me that it was profoundly emotional and extraordinarily freeing.

This led me to think that self identity problems could well be solved in this way by simply standing in front of a mirror, looking into one's own eyes and tapping.

When you can do this in the nude and you're laughing with delight, you know you're done!

e. Things, Objects & Substances

Just as pictures can be used, and songs too if they serve to trigger the connection to negative emotions in your neurology, so can a variety of other objects and substances sometimes be even more effective than using an opening statement on it's own, especially if there are a lot of issues and aspects involved, or if finding the right words is difficult or impossible.

- One lady who felt very guilty following the death of a beloved pet, held its collar in her hand whilst tapping and released very many issues;

- A young man I know cured himself of his love pain by playing "our song" whilst tapping. The song defined what the relationship and having lost it was all about, far better than words ever could.

- For allergies in particular, holding, smelling or being in the presence of the substance that triggers the reaction can be very helpful indeed.

- This is also useful for releasing addictions, addictive cravings and the like.

* Please Note: If your allergy is very severe or your responses are very severe, you need to be careful with being in the presence of the trigger substance.

For extremely severe allergic reactions, please have trained medical personnel standing by before testing your changes fully.

f. Overwhelm

There are some points in our lives where there are so many issues crowding in at once, it's impossible to know where to start.

Tapping without using any focus whatsoever, other than "I fully and deeply accept myself" in the opening statement perhaps, allows your unconscious mind to direct the release to where it is most needed at the time; sometimes, the root issue that triggered the overwhelm can be identified and released as well.

5. Memory Retrieval

I have used EFT extensively to retrieve "forgotten", "missing" and repressed memories.

From my point of view this is an extremely safe way to go about doing this, as the therapist is not in a position where their suggestions could trigger "false memory syndrome" - the person just taps themselves for **"Even though I don't know what happened/can't remember what happened/can't recall the specific incident"** and takes note of any ideas that come up, memory flashes or even physical sensations that can trigger the recall.

I have found whilst working with clients that 7 times out of ten a memory will present itself during the course of tapping the round, or immediately afterwards.

Sometimes, instead of the memory you are trying to retrieve, a "pre-memory" will present itself instead - for example, one lady said, "I kept thinking of my Aunt Annie, but I can't see what she has to do with any of this." She then tapped for, "Even though I don't know what Aunt Annie has to do with this problem", and this led into the memory of a holiday where the Aunt was present and the event she was trying to discover, took place.

A gentleman who had been trying to discover the root cause for a neuro-somatic back pain unsuccessfully for many years using all manners of therapies, didn't get anything whilst asking the question and tapping other than "a weird feeling in my head".

Upon tapping for "This weird feeling in my head", he discovered a memory of having been punched by his older brother when he was very small, and having fallen onto a toy chest where he hurt his back.

Ever since then and for the past 45 years, the pain in his back re-occurred whenever there was a situation where he felt threatened by someone in authority; following the EFT session, the pain has gone and never returned.

If you are interested in finding root causes and as an individual person using EFT, you can use this question system to help you remember things more easily, and without fear, because whatever you may find in the cause of your exploration, you can rest assured that EFT will be there to help you deal with it and release any negative emotions from the recovered memories right away.

PART III - THE A-Z OF EFT APPLICATIONS

There is just so much you can do with EFT, I sometimes think that the applications are truly limitless!

The reason for this is of course that **EFT is essentially a "content free" process** that can be applied anywhere any problem has an emotional component – and to be honest here, I have yet to come across any kind of human problem that does not have an emotional component, or two, or three.

Beginners in EFT are sometimes astonished at the sheer simplicity of the actual EFT protocol and can't yet conceive of all the things you can DO with it.

I've likened the EFT process to having being given a paintbrush. Not very impressive to look at, but with a bit of practise and if you wanted to, you could created the Mona Lisa. You've got all the colours of the rainbow to choose from and you can paint anything you want – and all you need is your humble little paint brush and knowing how to use it!

This next section is here to firstly open your eyes to the potential of this simple, content free technique.

Secondly, it is designed to be a teaching set for you to learn the underlying concepts through my experiences with using EFT with a wide variety of people and a huge variety of problems. Each one of the sections is a piece for your learning and understanding of the technique and how to apply it with real problems; some aspects are repeated many times because they are central and important, and each case story has something relevant to contribute to the understanding of the process and how you use it to create change, healing and success.

I would therefore suggest that you read each section, even though at first glance it might not apply to you personally.

So now, here are some of the possible areas where you might like to apply EFT for yourself, your nearest and dearest, and/or your clients. The motto is:

"Try it on EVERYTHING!"

EFT & Affirmations

Affirmations are statements of intent phrased in the positive and repeated many times, to imbed a positive belief deeply into the unconscious mind.

Examples of affirmations you may be familiar with are: "Every day, in every way, I'm getting better and better" and the famous, "I like myself!" in front of the bathroom mirror in the morning.

When people who have heard of or have been using affirmations come across the opening statements and the repeated reminder phrases, which are usually as negative as you can possibly get, they wonder if it isn't dangerous to say things like, "I really hate my body", "I'm absolutely terrified of the dark" and, "Even though I cannot believe that life could ever get better for me" and then to repeat these many times as the points are tapped.

It is very important to understand that the opening statement and the reminder phrases are NOT affirmations.

EFT opening statements are keys to problems which may have been buried in the deepest vaults of our neurology for many, many years.

They speak to parts of us that really feel this negative stuff is true, and who are always left out when positive affirmations are being made - EFT statements are designed to speak to them in the words that they recognise, to get in touch with them, and finally, to allow the balancing effect to take place which will heal them.

When these parts have been healed, positive affirmations take hold easily because there is no longer internal resistance which forces them to bounce off or to create internal conflict.

Using EFT To Strengthen Affirmations

Now, with this having been cleared up, you can of course use affirmation type opening statements because this will resolve some of the conflicts you might have about the affirmation and it's contents, such as:

- lack of belief in the affirmation,
- resistance to what you are affirming,
- conflicts with your self concept,
- reasons as to why the goal isn't such a good idea after all,
- old memories and previous decisions that are contrary to the affirmation.

You can use any affirmation or goal setting statement such as

- "I am beautiful",
- "I am rich",
- "I am loved",
- "My immune system is functioning superbly now",
- "People will buy my products and services in droves", etc.

What can happen when you do this that the **blockages and problems** with the desired goals come to light during the round of EFT or shortly afterwards; you can then treat the "problem statements" in the usual way before returning to the central affirmation.

If you don't get any resistance ideas to the affirmation **yet you have not reached the goal in practicality and you have been trying for a very long time**, you can elicit more on the topic by appending the affirmation with the word "but", "because", or even just "and" and see what turns up.

Also see "EFT & Personal Development", "EFT & Louise Hay" and "EFT & Conflict".

EFT & Addictions

It is now generally held that addictions of any kind, be they to certain activities such as gambling, exercising or internet chat groups; to substances of one kind or the other, or in the guise of overeating, to mention but a few, are not the problem. They are just a symptom, a way to cope with a deep underlying anxiety.

There are many levels and applications of using EFT to help overcome addictions.

At the most basic level, there is the simple reduction or elimination of cravings.

In seminars, Gary brings forth pieces of delicious chocolate and has the participants experience how tapping can eliminate the desire for this unhealthy substance. People who have been craving chocolate for years are absolutely astonished to find that not only they no longer want it, it doesn't smell good to them anymore and when they try to eat it, they don't even like the taste. For a minority of people, this can be a one-trial learning: after just one tapping for the craving for the substance, they never touch it again.

For others, it's not quite as straightforward as that; the craving may return after a while, and, interestingly, many "choose" to not use EFT on the problem ever again.

One lady during the course of one of my seminars tapped away her cravings for cigarettes, and then had a panic attack on the spot - there was a deep-seated belief that she simply couldn't cope with life without them.

With this lady, there were numerous statements required to undo a lifelong addiction (she had only stopped thumb sucking when she took up smoking, as it transpired); and many of the issues revolved around a literal fear that she would die if she didn't have her cigarettes. In this case, the cravings were not really the issue, but when the other things had been resolved and her fears had been laid to rest, she was at a point where she could "allow" EFT to help her with the problem and use its capacity to eliminate the cravings.

It is an interesting note that many who use EFT for almost everything else on a daily basis do not "choose" to use it on a major addiction problem such as alcohol, smoking, eating, or over working, to mention but a few. They are aware of the problem at the conscious level, and might even make many conscious decisions to start using EFT on the problem. But when comes down to actually doing it, all of a sudden they find that it's far more important to water the plants, make a telephone call or do just about anything else but start to tap for the problem! This is not a character defect, but a simple indication that there is massive internal opposition to the idea of even approaching the problem (see Psychological Reversal, Part 1, and Willpower, in this A-Z).

A useful way I have found around this is to tap, "Even though I don't want to (give up this addiction, lose weight, stop smoking, get fit), I deeply and profoundly accept myself" each day for a week or so.

This loosens up deep-seated fears like the ones of the lady with the cigarettes I mentioned earlier, and brings up the main objections to be dealt with gently as and when you're ready to do so.

With addictive behaviours in particular, there are aspects of self identity involved. Many times, doing some pre-work before starting on the actual addiction itself is a very ecological way forward. "How do I feel about having this problem?" and questions of this nature in general will also clear the way for a successful treatment.

Tapping for the underlying anxiety in general, and learning to become attuned for signs of one's own levels of rising anxiety, can often clear the way to overcoming addictions and is most helpful in this context.

Tapping can also be employed to deal with the perceived positive aspects of all addictive behaviours. "Even though the only time I feel truly happy is when …" can help undo unwanted positive feelings towards the addictive behaviours and/or substances. See also EFT & Primary Gain.

Lastly, investigating the why and wherefores of how the anxiety behind the addiction originated, and eliminating root causes with EFT, is of course a central approach for all addictive behaviours.

Please Note: Some addictions have deep and serious reasons and it might be necessary to visit with a trained practitioner to dismantle the relationship with the addiction over a period of time as the layers of dependency and their reasons become apparent.

Addiction Treatment is an important module in the AMT Practitioner Certification Training and some trainers also offer stand alone addictions trainings for this reason. Visit http://theamt.com for further information or to make contact with a trained and qualified practitioner.

EFT & Allergies

The number of people who have cured themselves entirely of such things as hay fever, dietary allergies, pet allergies to name but a few using nothing more than a few rounds of EFT, is legion.

According to some, allergies are nothing more and nothing less than a complete panic reaction by the auto immune system to the presence of a fairly harmless substance.

Try it on every allergy that comes your way.

There is nothing to be lost, and a lifetime of freedom to be gained. (see also Memories at the beginning of this section).

You can use:

- a simple **statement of the problem**, such as "Even though I am allergic to (…) ..",

- treat **the symptoms**, such as, "My nose is running uncontrollably ..."

- or, if the **root cause** is known to you, you can deal with that using any of the memory approaches.

Test yourself carefully before exposing yourself fully to the allergen, and should there be any reaction remaining, keep tapping until it is completely gone.

An Important Safety Note: If a reaction to an allergen is extreme or extremely severe, <u>do not expose yourself or your clients to the allergen</u> unless there is a trained paramedic/health care provider standing by.

EFT & Bereavement

Apart from love pain, perhaps, bereavement is one of the most painful of human states and emotions. I would like to take this opportunity to note that bereavement doesn't only occur when someone dies, but can also present when someone moves away, divorces or simply leaves.

As far as I am concerned, EFT is the ONLY treatment form that has ever significantly helped me with my own personal bereavement problems.

You may remember from the introduction that my first EFT experience came along as a result of tapping on "This ever-present sadness", and a memory flashed up - me standing in a sub zero midwinter church, staring at my father's coffin.

He had always loved red roses. His birthday had been in June; roses were glorious and always plentiful and on the mornings of his birthdays, my mother and I had presented him with a beautiful bouquet, the exact amount of roses according to the years he had been on this earth.

But now, he was dead, it was in the depth of January, and the few sad hothouse roses we had managed to scrape up were already withered, pathetic and dying in the intense cold.

At that point, my mind must have left my body because I didn't remember anything after that until much later, speaking to people at the wake.

EFT restored the missing memories and I can now begin to feel emotions other than intense pain when thinking about my father; something I for which I will be forever grateful.

Bereavement related problems are made up of such shock and trauma moments like the one I've just described; and then there are all the other reminders and sadnesses - so many negative emotions.

One lady came to see me because her husband of 56 years marriage had died quite unexpectedly. It quickly became apparent to me that there were so many issues, we might be tapping forever.

Further, there were practical problems, such as this lady having never been alone in a house, ever before in her life and becoming very seriously depressed and suicidal.

I decided to suggest to her to try the photograph release, and whenever she was alone at home and felt sadness or panic or despair arising, to go into the bedroom, look at the photograph of her husband, and just tap whilst looking at it and without saying anything at all.

She told me,

"The first week, I think I was getting sore from all the tapping. It was an absolute lifeline. I can't imagine what I would have ever done without it. Finally I could sleep again and I found it possible to start arranging some of our affairs. Now, three months on, I only tap once in a while with the picture. Most of the time, when I get a rush of weeping or sadness, it's quite enough for me to look at the picture and I can feel myself calming down. Really, I don't know if I would be here at all without the tapping."

I've said it before and will say it again - **EFT is there for you when you need it most.**

You don't have to find the strength to see a therapist in a moment of need, you can help yourself in any moment of crisis.

And many people have told me that it is the knowledge that they can help themselves, which in and of itself makes life's inevitable challenges so much easier to deal with.

EFT & Business

A short time ago, I visited a friend who runs a one-man business.

It was Monday morning, and I thought this would be a good time to talk with him about a couple of things, but I had to wait because he was desperately trying to persuade a money collector to not drag off part of his stock. I was astonished. I had not realised that things were this bad for him and felt guilty that I hadn't thought to phone him before.

The money collector eventually left, and my friend sat down on a box, on the verge of tears. He was absolutely desolate and terribly disappointed; he spent the best part of the last five years building the business, working all the hours God sends, putting his heart, mind and soul into it and now it had all gone horribly wrong.

During the next three hours (where no customer called or visited, but the answer phone took four messages from the bank and various suppliers) I tried to discover what had happened and if there was any prospect of salvaging anything from this disaster.

It is true that wherever I go these days, I'm wearing my "listen to what they say, for it holds the key to their problems" hat.

And listening to him talk, there were all the statements predicting failure:

- **"I'm just no good with figures, I knew this accounting would get me in the end,"**
- **"I guess I don't deserve success"**
- **"I just don't have the luck"**
- **"Everything I touch, goes wrong"**
- **"This has been yet another disappointment"**
- **"Who was I to think I could ever make something of myself."**
- **"Dreams are meant to be broken"**
- **"Me and my castles in the air, when will I ever come down to reality"**

- **"I should have listened to my father, he told me right from the start it was a stupid idea."**
- **"Nobody will be surprised to see me having failed again"**

Virtually every sentence he said to me would have made an excellent EFT opening statement in the context of "How to use EFT to overcome blockages to a successful career in business".

To cut a long story short, I helped him get over his deep moment of depression, and by the time I left, we had shored up the situation and he was on the telephone, calling on customers whom he had helped in the past in a variety of ways to ask for referrals and orders, enabled to do so by a few minutes of tapping for, "Even though I have to become successful all by myself and without help from anyone". I can't say he's out of the woods, or that we can be sure his current business will survive or even prosper, but he is being extremely sensible and pro-active and seems to have re-discovered some of the missionary zeal he had possessed when he first started out in business.

It's no overestimation to say that success in business has everything to do with the person's attitudes, values and beliefs.

We all know the amazing "rags to riches" stories, that tell us clearly that it's not a matter of being born lucky, being born wealthy, having a good education, having all the right breaks, etc. but that it's clearly a matter of how congruent we are within ourselves that we really deserve to be amongst the winners.

Whatever your line of work, whatever your line of business, take notice of what you think and what you say.

The world is such that you will always make it come true.

EFT & Children

One morning, I noticed that my teenage son had not yet started to play his extremely thudding brand of music.

Understandably alarmed, I went to his room, knocked on the door and a weak voice asked me to enter. He was in bed, looked terrible, and his face was hot and bright red. I sat down on the bed beside him, and as I asked him how he felt, I just gently massaged the points on his head and his fingers in turn - he knew what I was up to but was too weak to resist.

Within minutes, his skin colour had returned to normal, his temperature had gone down and he was getting up. A bit of TLC, EFT or the combination of both?

What I'm trying to say is that there are a hundred and one ways in which I use EFT with my own children, as and when required.

- ❖ Last week, my 9 year old came home, utterly upset because he had been teased by a group of children. He was trying really hard not to cry but he had been hurt badly. I sat him down and tapped him, and within a few minutes he was calm enough to talk to me, to discuss various reasons why these sort of things happen, and how to avoid them in future. Half an hour later and he was fine.

- ❖ The same boy used to be badly travel sick. Applying EFT in the back seat of the car with someone else driving took care of that in one session lasting less than 15 minutes.

- ❖ The older boy used to have a phobia of all things dead. I have no idea as to the root cause of this, but it started when he was about 8 or 9 and it was intense.

- ❖ He could never watch any horror movies in case there were any hint of vampires or zombies, and woe betide there should be a dead bird or mouse dragged in by the cats. One day, our oldest dog died in her sleep, and my son used tapping with my help to lay the fear to rest. He was able to sit next to the body of the dog,

77

stroke her and say goodbye. The next day, he actively and all by himself, sought out a large spider to overcome that fear, too.

These are just a few personal testimonials from me; my friends, colleagues and clients have all used EFT with their own children with amazing results.

One of my colleagues said during the course of an interview, "To have been given the power to help our own children when they are in pain, ill or upset, is intense."

EFT is not a talking therapy and therefore it can be used with non-verbal and pre-verbal children, too.

One interesting application is to have the mother tap herself for the problem of the child, using surrogate or proxy tapping (see also EFT Terms, Part IV).

Instead of tapping on the child directly, the mother taps herself and says,

> **"I am my child. I am terrified of dogs**
> **and I deeply and profoundly love and accept myself,"**

... for example.

In this way a number of issues have been most successfully resolved.

Nick Westwood, a fellow hypnotherapist, says, "I find this proxy tapping most fascinating. It has a **double effect** when used with mothers or fathers and their children.

"Not only does it often produce healing shifts in the children, the tapping also relaxes the parent and they find it easier to cope with the problems that come with illness or behavioural difficulties in children.

"One lady found it most healing to sit with her premature baby, whom she could not touch, and tap, knowing that it would possibly help him pull through. At the same time, she was keeping herself from descending into blind panic and anxiety. It's a wonderful gift to all parents."

Helping The Parent, Helping The Child

It is a truth that of course, we want our children to be as perfect as possible, and it is very frightening on very many levels when they are not.

A practitioner of EFT was working with his daughter, age 10, on her lack of abilities in reading and writing. The girl was resistant to the treatment and it didn't show much in the way of results; so he contacted me for further help.

I suggested that before he started the next session with his daughter to go somewhere quiet to address all HIS feelings about the daughter being "behind in class".

He was surprised at this advice but followed it; this is what he wrote to me two days later.

"I want to thank you for this breakthrough. It was not until I actually started to tap myself that I became aware of how important this was to me, how afraid I was for her to be failing not just in school, but in life, and how I had let this one issue dominate my thoughts and my relationship with my daughter.

"She is a wonderful child – caring, intelligent, she tries so hard at everything she does.

"Following my self treatment, I called her to me and told her that I loved her for who she was, that I didn't care if she'd never learn to spell correctly, that I was so proud to have her be my daughter, and that I wouldn't come after her with all these different treatments anymore, that she was perfect just the way she was.

"We both ended up crying. The next day, she came to me and asked if we could try the EFT again. We tapped together on her fear, disappointment, hurt and feeling that she was not as good as the other children in class and it was a real breakthrough in every way for both of us."

Is this child's reading now at Superman levels?

I don't know. To be honest, I don't even care. There's more to life than being able to read as fast as everyone else; the girl is only ten and she has another 90 years or so to practise.

There are things though that she doesn't have another 90 years time to learn about, and one of them is that you are worthy of your father's love and admiration, just for who you are and NOT for what you can, what you look like or what random marks some stranger decides to bestow on your efforts.

When a parent releases **their own fears** in regards to their children's problems, something very profound and important happens to their relationship – it is as though a tension has been resolved that clears the way for all sorts of new developments, for new growth and in the end, for very profound healing.

Children Treating Themselves

Children from as young as three years old can learn to tap themselves quite easily.

One little girl who had been very shy and withdrawn, said, "When I pat on the healing buttons, my tummy feels better right away." Another little boy who used to live in fear of being bullied at school found it most helpful too, and called the procedure, "Like having a guardian angel." Interestingly, once he stopped being afraid, the bullies went on to find themselves another target.

There is a lovely story of a 7 year old being seen teaching EFT to a 5 year old in a school playground so that the little boy stopped crying following a fall.

Being able to do the EFT treatment for yourself, even an abbreviated version if necessary, gives children a whole new degree of control and possibilities of control over themselves and their lives. Especially for school children who are under such enormous pressure from parents, teachers and peers, being pushed and dragged into all these different directions, having to struggle with concentration, difficult materials, motivation issues and social problems all the while, being able to use

EFT as and when needed is simply worth it's weight in gold. *See also "Learning" and "Social Phobia".*

Treating Children With EFT

In general, EFT is simple enough; the trick is always to find a way to explain the basic facts in such a way that the person (small or big) you are explaining it to understands and sees the sense in it all.

I have used explanations such as, "There are these power lines in your body, and feelings and bad things make them get stuck. You tap on them loosen them up where they are stuck and then it all flows freely again and you feel better."

Another one I use quite often is this metaphor, "You know a chain of Christmas Tree lights – you tap all the bulbs and when you get the right one, all the lights come on and it's working perfectly again."

You can call the tapping points "switches" or "buttons"; you can show children EFT diagrams with the points marked out on a favourite cartoon character, football hero, singer or a movie star to create a sense of comfort and recognition.

With small children, you can show them the points on a favourite doll or teddy bear; one very shy and withdrawn boy of 6 years old had his first breakthrough experiences by tapping on his teddy bear and making up opening statements for "teddy" such as, "Even though teddy is afraid of the dark, I think he's a great teddy." This is an approach not to be underestimated. Children who do have a real favourite toy such as this **invest a great deal of themselves** into these toys and although we are not really treating real meridians, it is absolutely a full, functional and working treatment on many other levels.

One little girl had the tapping points painted onto her face by me with a lipstick and tapped herself whilst looking in the mirror and giggling all the while; it's all about finding a simple way that fits in with the particular child so they learn the points and get to find out for themselves that they can help you feel better if you tap on them.

If a child is having real problems expressing themselves in words, you can replace a verbal set up with having the child do a drawing of the problem, or by placing one hand on the area "where it hurts" (that works for emotional pain as well as physical pain) whilst tapping with the other. Remember also the "keyword" approach – sometimes just saying the word, "School", for example, will do the trick without having to go into any further details.

The standard SUDs level readings are replaced by having a child show you with their hands how big a problem it is, like a fisherman would show the size of the fish, before and after the treatments. That is a wonderful feedback device so you can both really SEE how the problem is shrinking.

One final note on the subject of children. For the parent to tap for, "Even though Sam has this problem, I deeply and profoundly accept him and I love him unconditionally" is a small incident of pure magic and I recommend this highly to all parents, no matter the problem, or even if there isn't one at all.

EFT & Chromotherapy

Just before I got "into" EFT, I purchased a set for Crystal Light Balancing & Chromotherapy (colour healing). In this modality, you use a little torch with coloured filters and a crystal tip to trace along the major meridians to unblock them and I was fascinated by the spontaneous recall of traumatic memories that would sometimes occur (not to mention the fact that the torch doesn't half look like one of those Star Trek healing devices when the lights are low and you're using green or purple filters :-).

Since EFT, I've used the torch to good effect on various people who like that kind of thing; some who for some reason or other didn't like being touched; and a premature baby. Instead of tapping on the points, I shine the torch on the EFT points; as you also have a choice of the different colours, it makes the selection of colours and trying out their different effects on the EFT points a fascinating exercise.

With my particular chromotherapy set there came a manual, which shows the location of the main meridians and also offers a nice explanation of the more spiritual/emotional side of what they do. I find it quite interesting and refer to it often.

Chromotherapy Workbook & Torches available from Renascent, PO Box 160, Nunawading, 3131, Australia.

More on EFT and Meridians can be found in Ananga Sivyer's book, The Art & Science of Emotional Freedom, available from http://theamt.com

EFT & Conflict

A very interesting EFT application is to be able to deal with conflicts between two or more issues.

Oftentimes, it is not "one thing" or "the other" that is the problem, but the conflict and tension that exists between them.

One of my clients was very angry with their mother and we treated the anger with no noticeable benefit by the way of the client relaxing or getting any more resolved on the various issues and problems.

It occurred to me to have them tap on both sides of the argument in the same statement:

I hate my mother AND I love my mother.

It was quite extraordinary to watch what happened next; when the conflict resolved, the client just softened all over, heaved a huge sigh of relief that turned into a long, drawn out yawn and reported a sense of peace that had eluded them for many, many years.

Since then, I have made it a habit to tap on "both sides of the coin" as a rule, just to be on the safe side, when there was a sense of conflict, such as depression, a feeling of stuckness or stalemate, behaviours that go backs and forth between extremes in cycles, and especially in the treatment of addictions.

For example, on the topic of weight loss, food is both the best friend and the worst enemy both and at the same time.

In many situations, the problem doesn't lie in one thing or the other, but when you try to combine the two, you have a truly nasty conflict on your hands:

I hate my job and I need to keep my job.

... for example.

If the person just hated their job, they could walk away and find another one, so that's not a problem.

If they just needed to keep their job, that wouldn't be a problem either – the problem comes when the two exist together.

This is particularly pertinent to many relationship issues where the conflicts and STUCKNESS often occurs for just this type of conflict:

"I can't live without him **and** he's destroying me."

Other versions of such conflict pairs, triangles and groups can be found by using other connecting words such as "but", "although", and also, "because".

- I am terribly unhappy in this marriage **but** I'm stuck in it.

- I want to travel **although** I really should stay with my children.

- I can never get well **because** I was born this way **and** I don't deserve any better.

In general EFT treatments, you would treat each part of these sentences by themselves; if you've tried this on conflict issues and it has not resolved the feeling of tension and stuckness, I highly recommend doing these combination opening statements and reminder phrases.

Like with many things, in combination they become more and **other** than the sum of their parts when you put them together.

To resolve that conflict can help tremendously and go a long way to a true resolution of many problems.

EFT & Creativity

I have a notion that we are all born superbly creative, because young children are so very creative in their thinking; for some of us unfortunately, school, life and unhappiness in general then bashes it out of us at a later date.

Some people have set out to use EFT to further their creative endeavours; amongst the examples that spring to mind is a young man who suffered from Writer's Block and resolved this in one simple session; and a sculptor who, following the application of EFT to resolve his problems in that area, had such a flood of new ideas that he was up for a day, a whole night, and part of the next day, writing them all down frantically just in case this was a glitch and his block would come back at a later date!

Other EFT users have found access to creativity by chance and accident.

Lianne, a middle aged lady, came to see me for a fear of public speaking. She had been recently promoted at work and now needed to do presentations for groups and supervise trainings but was petrified at the prospect. As with so many people, this fear had begun at school where a teacher had ridiculed her in front of the whole class. Her public speaking was a great success after the treatment but there was an unforeseen side effect. The root cause event way back in her school days had had another and, for me, horrifying repercussion. The public dressing down revolved around an art project which apparently had "not been good enough". Up until that point, Lianne had loved art, spent much of her time drawing and painting and had even dreamed of going to art school when she was older.

After the incident she had quietly put her paints and brushes away and had never touched anything relating to creativity again. She told me this because one day, a week or so after the treatment, she had found herself absentmindedly drawing on her telephone notepad - something she had not done for over 30 years.

Here's yet another aspect to creativity: in any given field, be it management, science, computing or art and literature, it seems to be that at the bottom and in the middle of the field, you get rewarded for doing things "by the book" and according to a set standard and tradition. But if you want to get right to the top and become a leader in the field, all of a sudden intense creativity becomes a "must".

Without it, you are doomed to re-cycle other more creative peoples' ideas forever.

James was in just that position. He had worked hard all his life, thoroughly learned everything there was to be learned, studied and studied, worked his way up the ranks and was now set to move into the "leader" position.

However, in order to be able to do so, he had to come up with new ideas, creative endeavours and a completely different set of skills to those he had employed for over 25 years to get to where he was today.

He had been passed over for promotion to the top position twice already and feared that he "would never be anything else than an also ran - I just don't have what it takes". I've been working with him on and off for a while to help him overcome a lifetime of partitioning off feelings, intuitions and creativity, and he is beginning to find a whole new lease of life.

Creativity is not something that should be restricted to artists.

It is something that allows one to **find extraordinary solutions to everyday problems**, to conduct relationships in an exciting fashion, and can make all the difference to one's chosen career, life, and levels of happiness.

EFT & Dreams

Nightmares

Bad dreams and nightmares are a very disturbing proposition; it's always well to keep in mind that these are manifestations and symptoms of an underlying problem, and never a problem in and of themselves.

You can approach bad dreams in a number of different ways.

The first one may be to tap before going to sleep and express a desire to sleep soundly and well - "I desire to sleep deeply and I deeply and profoundly accept myself". As you do this, objections may come up in your mind, or even feelings of dread or disbelief. You can then tap on these "Even though I am afraid I will have a nightmare ." or, "Even though there's something bothering me in my sleep ."

Probably the most ecological way to deal with recurrent bad dreams that follow a theme is to tap for the dream experiences and feelings as though they were "real" memories:

- "Even though there is this monster chasing me, ."
- "Even though I am so afraid of the monster ."
- "Even though I know the monster is going to kill me."

Using this approach, the problems may be cleared without having to deal with the underlying issue in consciousness at all, which can be helpful if the subject matter the dreams relate to is particularly distressing or results from repressed memories of traumatic events.

For those who need to know the reasons for the nightmares or bad dreams, tapping for insights using statements such as, "Even though I don't know what the monster represents ..."

If you use this approach, don't be disappointed if you don't realise it right away in the course of the round or immediately afterwards. Sometimes the realisation or mental connection comes the next day, the day after that, or even in a further dream as you sleep.

Using the "I don't know" form of opening statement will eventually get you there; sometimes, there's some other blockage that needs to be resolved first, so be on the lookout for other problems that spring to mind even if they seem completely unrelated. Unrelated thoughts and ideas are often "pre-memories" that lead to what you are trying to discover.

If you already know what events have caused the nightmares, or you have found a correlation in time to the onset of the nightmares and an obvious candidate for a reason, such as bereavement, moving house, or a traumatic experience or accident of any kind, tapping for the underlying cause will generally resolve the need to have the nightmares as well.

Waking in the night or the next morning with negative feelings that are the residue of the bad dreams can give an opportunity to work with the dominant emotion that is present, whether this may be fear, dread, anxiety, panic, desperation, pain or whatever else you can sense within you. Tapping on the particular feeling whilst it is still present and strong in your mind may also relieve the root causes for the bad dreams.

For small children or others that won't/can't tap for themselves, proxy tapping any of the approaches above can be very helpful indeed. I know of three people who have successfully "cured" their children of bad dreams using the proxy tapping approach; only one of them knew the underlying cause and tapped for that, the other two used simple opening statements such as, "Even though Mandy has bad dreams, I deeply and profoundly love and accept Mandy."

Lucid Dreaming, Dream Recall & "Lovely" Dreams

Just as nightmares in the night make the next day much harder to deal with, wonderful dreams make the next day sparkling and bright.

Try tapping a round or two expressing a desire to experience a particularly wonderful dream that will let you contact resources of happiness, creativity, love and excitement is well worth a try even if you sleep very well already.

Dream recall and lucid dreaming can be greatly aided by tapping on any existing objections to such an endeavour, be it of the "Even though I don't know how to improve my lucid dreaming/dream recall skills ." variety, or by unblocking any existing limiting beliefs such as "Even though I can't recall my dreams easily." - "I'm afraid what I might learn about myself if I recalled my dreams ." - "Only special people can learn lucid dreaming ." or whatever might be your dominant limiting thoughts on the subject.

Finally on the subject of dreams, here's a case story:

The Fly Master

A lady came to see me because she had been suffering from a recurrent nightmare for the past five years. A dark and very frightening apparition which was not human would dispatch swarms of big black flies towards her which would try and get into her brain through her ears. In the dreams, she would run and try desperately to defend herself from the flies but some would eventually get through and enter her ears at which point she would awake screaming and bathed in sweat.

She had never told anyone about this because she was afraid they would think she was crazy, and as she related the dream she began to cry, shake and was obviously very upset indeed.

She tapped a first round with the set up, "Even though I am petrified of the Fly Master" and calmed significantly, yawned and yawned again. Another round of tapping which centred on her feelings of helplessness produced more yawning and she was now very relaxed and calm.

It then occurred to her spontaneously that this might be related to a boyfriend she had lived with up until five years ago, who was interested in black occult, and who had threatened on more than one occasion that he would find ways to "get her" and that there would be nowhere to hide. Following this insight, she tapped for, "Even though I don't believe I can protect myself from psychic attacks" until she felt that she could trust her unconscious mind to protect her perfectly well.

The nightmares stopped and have not returned; if her fears were real or imagined was, as usual, of no importance. The important thing was that the tapping set her free from what might be called a "post-hypnotic suggestion" by the ex-boyfriend that had haunted her since she had dared to leave him.

Dream Interpretation

Have you ever had a dream that was so bright and vivid, and clearly remembered, and you just **knew** it was very important somehow but you just cannot work out "what it means"?

Dream interpretation used to be a very special occupation that was deemed to be so important that only the best and highest priests would get to do this for others. Nowadays, just about everyone interested in health, healing and psychology has a Dream book on their shelves – a kind of dictionary that assigns meanings to symbols and objects encountered in dreams, to help the dreamer "get the message" from that other part of their mind. To be honest, I really don't know what happens in a person's mind or in their energy system when one taps on opening statements such as "Even though I have no idea at all why me standing watching a boat go by should be so very important."

However, what does happen very regularly is that all of a sudden, some new ideas and insights seem to bubble their way to the surface – ideas about how the dream symbols were connected with real life events, current and past, and what messages this dream might hold. It is extremely surprising and very interesting to do this and very deep and meaningful insights can be derived from this. Often, treating a dream in such a way with EFT – or should I say, treating the dreamer – shows up that the original thoughts and interpretations were way off the mark. See also EFT & Metaphors on this topic.

EFT & Fear Of Flying

I treated a good friend of mine for her airplane phobia over the phone one evening about two years ago. I shouldn't have done that.

I basically haven't seen her since.

She's all over the world, flying here, there and everywhere.

Here are some special tips on EFT & Airplane Phobias and Fear of Flying:

- If you can remember the first time it happened, go through the memories of that event in your mind or tell the story out loud by yourself or with a friend. You can soon spot the statements and thoughts that cause you the greatest distress or emotional response. Tap on these until you can think/talk about these events and remain calm and focussed.

- Sometimes, there are "triggers" in the environment you can use to treat fears before you get anywhere near an airplane. One lady used a television programme about planes and helicopters to begin her treatment, a gentleman used to feel nauseous when seeing planes in the sky. With one particular gentleman the fear began when he booked the ticket in the travel agent's office.

- To make sure you have removed all your fears successfully, imagine going on a particular journey in detail, right from packing the bags to taking the taxi to the airport, to going through the doors and smelling that unique "airport" smell, to the waiting period, onto the plane, and imagine a bumpy ride in bad weather, even with people screaming, if you will. If at any time you become distressed or anxious, stop and tap on that "aspect" of your general fear of flying until you feel calm and it no longer bothers you.

- If you sense any nervousness returning, use the waiting time in airports to treat yourself surreptitiously, or go to the toilet and treat yourself where no-one can see you. In public, you can just hold or lightly massage the points and take a deep breath on each one so no-one will ever know what you're up to.

- After a short time, most people find they have "favourites" amongst the points in the list above, i.e. points that are more effective than others. Use these for shortcuts or in moments of panic.

You can also use EFT very successfully to treat yourself for jet lag symptoms of all kinds, and for general travel stress and travel sickness. This will keep you feeling calmer and much less stressed and makes it much less likely that you should experience immune system breaches such as stomach upsets, sore throats, or flare ups of other stress related illnesses on holiday or business travels.

93

EFT & Giving Up Smoking

Amazing though it may seem, smoking cessation treatments are still a vast industry and some hold cigarette smoking addictions to be one of the most profoundly difficult addiction to treat.

Without EFT, this may indeed be so; but luckily, in EFT we have the central tool to help anyone who is ready to take this step towards freedom to do so cleanly, elegantly and without suffering anxiety and withdrawal.

This is a wonderful gift and proposition for many people who have struggled with a smoking addiction for a long time in many ways; not least of all to reverse their idea that they "have no will power" or that they are somehow more deficient than their friends and colleagues who seemed to have no trouble at all and just gave up, just like that.

The truth is that for those people who cannot give up smoking, the emotional and energetic relationships and ties to the substance and ritualised activities surrounding smoking are simply far more intense and up to now, there really wasn't anything to help these people get free of their "emotional chains" which tied them to their smoking demon.

Here is a very thorough 7 Step protocol designed to really help and support a person who wishes to be free at last, and completely free forever to accomplish this with a minimum of fuss and no pain whatsoever – thanks to EFT.

Setting The Stage For Freedom

If someone is still not sure if they really want to give up smoking at all, thinking they might need it for something important even though you can't imagine what that might be, we can start the process of really get free from cigarettes by tapping on the following pre-cursors for a successful smoking abolition:

- I am not and I was never designed to breathe smoke.
- Cigarettes do not and have never protected me from life's ills, shocks and surprises.

94

- I don't know why I have smoked for so long, all I know is that I want to end it now.

Here is another set of stoppers to starting on the road to freedom:

- I am really afraid to have to face life without cigarettes.
- I have failed so many times before at giving up.
- I fear the struggles, pain, confusion and desperate longings for cigarettes.
- I will never be free of the need for cigarettes and it will be withdrawal forever.

Another set for some might be:

- I am not "giving in" to my mother, husband, spouse, the goody two-shoes of society etc. but rather, I'm setting myself free now.
- Giving up cigarettes does not mean I will change into another person. I will remain me.
- This is my decision, my choice. I want to breathe clean air and I want to be free.
- When I started to smoke, I really never signed up for a life time of financial, physical and emotional slavery. That's not what I ever wanted.

When we are at a point where the soon to become ex-smoker has made the firm and really positive decision all by themselves (i.e. without emotional blackmail from relatives, therapists, or whoever involved) and has released all and every good reason to needing to hold on to the smoking relationship they can think of and really are ready, keen and eager to go on into the practical exercises, we procede and no sooner than that.

1. The Cigarette Itself

Tap on the attraction to, need for or desire for lighting the cigarette. Hold it, smell it, and then tap on whatever opening statement comes to mind:

- "Even though I really, really want and need this cigarette ...."
- "Even though I have to have this cigarette ..."

95

- "Even though I need to have what this cigarette gives me ..."

For the sake of a super-tidy, all aspects picked up cleanly intervention, do the same with the packet. There is a lot of unconscious content tied into the packaging and probably the brand too, including unconscious linkages to advertisements of sport, success, coolness and so forth. Even though these advertisements may not now be around, they were at some time and still reside in the unconscious memory, adding to this particular brand's attractions.

2. The First Time We Ever Met ....

Now it's time to go down memory lane and to clear up the "falling in love with smoking" emotions, sensations, thoughts, feelings and meanings.

Whether it was feeling grown up and cool, rebellious, smart; whether it was smoking to help with eating less or feeling dizzy and different, better than the usual misery of normalness; whether the cigarette was the entrance ticket into a tightly bonded secret society of James Dean type characters; or whether it was being just like mummy, daddy and all the other powerful grown ups around – these first connections and first experiences are very, very powerful energetic bonds in body, mind and memory which will effectively tie someone to smoking and all it stands for, often for a lifetime.

3. Magic Moments ....

This is another set of related memories and events which are often overlooked in the treatment of smoking especially. Survivors of airplane disasters, for example, if they happen to be smokers, know that they are still alive and walking away from the tragedy when they light their first cigarette after the event.

It is also thus for women who just gave birth, people who have just been through a very traumatic session at work, after a car crash and so on and so forth.

There is more to these magic moments, too.

Smokers use the act and excuse of leaving to go for a cigarette to clear their minds, get space from overwhelm, give themselves time to think before they act, to calm themselves before a particularly stressful event.

What happens is that these magic moments become a part of smoking itself and tightly linked into the act of smoking – no cigarette, no survival. No cigarette, no reason to get out of stressful situations. No cigarette, no chance of thinking things through in solitude.

It is of course absolutely appalling that a ritual like smoking should have to come along to give people these much needed spaces and markers rather than some other form of behaviour or thought; and it is very important to come up with some ideas how to replace these forms of magic moment smoking activities with another so the need will be filled in future.

Interestingly, taking oneself off somewhere quiet to do a round of EFT or two can very effectively replace this important moment without resorting to having to smoke at all in many circumstances.

4. Physical Cravings & Traumatic Withdrawals

Most people have tried to give up smoking many times before and "failed". This is usually due to a rising feedback loop between actual physical cravings for nicotine and anxiety, each one pushing the other up and up and making for a very unpleasant experience indeed.

It only needs a few such unpleasant withdrawal experiences and what happens is that both the idea of future attempts becomes much more frightening, and that future withdrawal attempts get more traumatic and frightening faster each time this happens.

EFT very effectively breaks up this cravings-anxiety feedback loop and restores a sense of balance and tranquillity. Simply focussing on the physical feelings of anxiety whilst tapping the full protocol is of enormous help; but also, **knowing** that EFT is there to help reduce anxiety and the effects of withdrawal lowers the overall anxiety rate right up front.

Fascinatingly, once the anxiety is out of the way, the actual real physiological responses to a lack of nicotine in the system are massively reduced. The remaining physiological symptoms and experiences are really quite mild and even those can be alleviated into non-existence with EFT by focussing on or describing the sensation in the opening statement.

5. General Anxiety Treatments

Smokers can be nervous people who suffer from underlying stress and anxiety and have found that the ritualised acts of smoking, the "magic moment" withdrawing from stressful situations and the state shift cigarettes induce helps with that ever present sense of anxiety which pervades their lives.

Any EFT treatment to reduce the "background noise" anxiety levels in someone's life will help with being able to want to face life without the help smoking provides.

Finding opening statements about the things that are the greatest source of stress in a person's life, may they have to do with relationships, with work, with concerns about the self and one's path in life, is greatly helpful to make that move into freedom.

6. Breaking High Linkage Moments

There are certain times in every ex-smokers life where they are particularly vulnerable to "giving in to temptation" and unless these links are firmly broken, you might end up like some of these people who didn't smoke for many years and then fell straight back into it after just one repetition.

Going around and calling oneself a "recovering smoker" or a "smoke survivor" and needing to be afraid that the demon will return if the guard has been let down even for a single second does absolutely NOTHING to alley the general levels of anxiety smokers suffer from anyway and makes the whole idea into a nightmare.

98

It is to be clearly understood that EFT is absolutely capable of breaking up these linkages, for example after meals, with a cup of coffee, in a bar or after having consumed some alcohol.

The treatment in this case is to allow oneself to really experience the linkage cravings as deeply as possible and then to tap instead of lighting up – even if it starts just with a few taps under the eye or a surreptitious tap of the Karate Chop point when in a public situation.

Indeed, smokers should **practise** breaking up the withdrawal linkages in a quiet place at home; and those who experience the most "temptation" when other substances such as coffee or alcohol are present, should actively set this up so that they can get this most important work done in peace and quiet, and in their own time, so when the situation occurs for real, they are ready, prepared and know exactly what to do.

7. Long Term Limiting Beliefs & Old Wives Tales

The last aspect of treating a tobacco and smoking addiction extremely successfully, and most importantly, easily and without adding due stress and pain to someone's life is to deal with deep seated beliefs and old wives tales about smoking.

One of these would be the terrible toll on someone's health. Amazing as this may seem, there is actually no direct cause-and-effect linkage between how much any one given individual smokes and what kind of diseases they will get or exactly when they will get them (unlike say, arsenic, where the responses of any individual to the same dosage over time are very predictable indeed).

This leaves much room for using the neuro-somatic leverage of our mind-body totalities in the best interest for ex-smokers by removing beliefs about having to die of lung cancer, never being able to regain any form of fitness, it being too late for them now and so forth.

There are all sorts of beliefs around smoking, the effects, what it takes to give up, how long it takes, how painful it may be, and what becomes of people who do give up smoking successfully – and including with many people a deep seated fear that they will turn into some sandal wearing, mineral water slurping health freak!

We have already mentioned above the beliefs around "never really being free" of smoking once you have started and it is very important for every individual to find their own, to formulate them into an opening statement that makes sense, and simply to tap them away.

So here we are. Seven steps to use the power of EFT to really clear up the energy system and put a person into a position where they will choose freedom and personal power over being enslaved to a substance which, in the end, cannot be expected to solve their problems or protect them from the world.

EFT & Hypnosis

Is EFT Hypnosis?

Let's start here, which is a question I am asked quite regularly.

I am often asked by those who have not experienced EFT - Emotional Freedom Techniques - if it is a form of hypnosis or hypnotherapy.

What I always say is that actually, EFT is a form of acupuncture, only that the needles replaced by a person's own fingertips.

It is a **physiological process**, based on the meridian system, and it's effect lies in stimulating important junction points of main body meridians - the "EFT Tapping Points" – coupled with directing your attention towards the parts of the energy system you are trying to adjust.

EFT being both content free - the person who is treating themselves chooses what they are treating themselves for and concentrate on this by repeating a statement of the problem in question - and also extremely simple once learned, it is the perfect *adjunct* to many already existing therapies.

EFT is used both as a homework protocol to give a client to do at home, by themselves, any time to help with a treatment in progress, as well as being used to treat psychological problems in a therapeutic session, with a therapist teaching the EFT protocol and guiding the client through the process.

Amongst the practitioners using EFT as a part of their work are all helping and caring professions, such as:

- o Nurses
- o Care and Aid Workers
- o Psychologists
- o Massage Therapists
- o Hypnotherapists
- o Counsellors
- o Homeopaths
- o Herbalists

- o Acupuncturists
- o Medical Doctors
- o Dentists
- o Clinical Psychologists
- o Community Care Staff
- o Kinesiologists

... and indeed, the whole range of care providers both allopathic and holistic – and only very, very few of these are actually trained in hypnotherapy; as they are getting very good results across the board, this in and of itself more or less already proves that EFT is certainly something **other** than "just hypnosis".

EFT is, in spite of it's simplicity, a very profound process that has direct effects on a person's mind and body.

When a trained practitioner works with a client on an important, life changing issue, it is a **very intensive and often moving process** that might lead an outside observer to wonder whether there is more going on than just tapping the meridian points, and it is here where the word "hypnotherapy" comes in.

EFT is not hypnotherapy, no more so than a full body massage, a reflexology session or an acupuncture treatment.

Like these other physiologically based treatments, with a good practitioner it is an intensive experience and very emotional; and if one was to define "hypnotherapy" as any form of therapy where a client and practitioner work together with concentration, full focus on the problem and a good understanding between them, you could class EFT as such of course.

However, the simple facts are that:

- o EFT can be done by anyone at all, just by reading the instructions from a piece of paper, all by themselves, without any psychology knowledge or training whatsoever, and the vast majority of people experience a real shift in the problem they were working on under these circumstances. This is mainly why EFT is as successful as it is, and why it is spreading as rapidly as it

102

is. EFT has been called, "The best self help technique EVER." for this very reason.

o Clearly, without any practitioner present who could "suggest" anything, the process works very well.

o EFT is being taught and shown by hundreds and thousands of people around the world and the great majority have no experience of hypnotherapy at all. For example, Red Cross workers from Kosovo to Nigeria were taught the protocol and in turn, taught it to those they care for; these, in turn, taught their families, children and friends.

o EFT is so simple that a child can use it, AND a child can teach ANOTHER to use it.

o Lastly, and this is very important, EFT relies entirely and totally on ***what the user or client says*** - the tapping routine is always the same, every time. The difference in the individual treatments lies in the person's words who are using the treatment, and these words are *the person's own words* - even when there is a trained Meridian Energy Therapies practitioner present, all they do is ASK the client how they feel, what their problem is, to reveal the person's **OWN OPENING STATEMENTS**.

o There is nothing suggested, nothing added from the practitioner at all - all they do is to ELICIT an opening statement for the treatment from the client.

o With experience, a practitioner will become good at listening to a client and being able to pick out amongst all the words they said and phrases they used just what will make the most effective statement for the problem - but the **WORDS ARE ALWAYS THE CLIENT'S OWN WORDS.**

Indeed, much time is spent in the training of practitioners who may have been counsellors for many years and who are used to rephrasing what the client said into their own words that this doesn't work with EFT - the client has to say what ails them and how they feel IN THEIR OWN WORDS and only then does the treatment work as it was designed to be.

This is a unique and wonderful thing, for EFT thus puts the keys to the problem AND the solution right back where it belongs - namely with each individual person themselves.

In conclusion, I would like to draw your attention to something the creator of EFT, Gary Craig, says in his seminars right at the beginning.

He says,

"Please try and keep an open mind. EFT is not like anything you have experienced before - it is really a NEW experience. Don't judge it in terms of it being this, or that. Keep an open mind, try it for yourself and then, and only then, will you know just what it is."

Now that we have established that EFT in and of itself is not hypnosis, I would like to talk about actually and deliberately **combining EFT with hypnosis** because simply, there are many ways in which a knowledge of the processes of hypnosis can help and speed up EFT treatments and make treatment sessions feel more gentle to the clients who experience them.

Hypnosis & EFT

There are so many ways EFT and hypnosis can work together - I hope you will have some fun with this section and try out some of these things, whether you are a hypnotherapist or not.

For hypnotherapists, doing EFT with a client whilst they are in a trance state can be most interesting and helpful to shift deep blockages and problems.

The application of EFT in and of itself and in the absence of any further deepening techniques **leads to a light trance state** and even more so if a therapist does the actual tapping; it can thereby be used as an easy trance induction which doubles as a treatment at the same time.

In a typical hypnosis session, it can be used at any point to help soothe and alleviate emotions arising, or to gentle away any blockages you might run into; and of course, it can be used as a profound deepener at any stage of an induction.

EFT can help people to be able to experience hypnosis in the first place.

Many people who don't seem to get much from it, or find it hard or impossible to relax, can use EFT to overcome limiting fears and beliefs first: "Even though I am afraid of losing control," - "Even though hypnosis doesn't work for me" - "Even though I'm not sure I will be able to resist suggestions that are against my own values".

Removing such blocks opens the way for anyone to have access to helpful hypnosis tapes, pain and drug free dentistry, childbirth and surgery, and not to mention auto-suggestion, autogenics, self hypnosis, SuperLearning, meditation and deep relaxation.

EFT & Intuition

The first time I encountered the very idea that EFT might be used to open up one's further senses and channels was at an introduction evening, where one of the participants decided they wanted to "reclaim their second sight". Apparently, this lady lived with a flatmate who was a very successful dowser and had been told many times by tarot readers and clairvoyants that she also possessed such gifts but she could not find any way to access them in spite of much practice and meditation.

She tapped on, "Even though I don't know how to use the second sight" and reported that she had been thinking of birds all the way through the round - big, black birds.

Trusting that her unconscious mind had come up with the reason, even if we didn't understand what it meant, she tapped for, "Even though I have this bird problem".

Halfway through the round, she began to yawn - always an indication that something is being released - and then reported that she had had nightmares for many years as a child where birds would come and peck out her eyes; this had stopped around the time of puberty and she had quite forgotten about it.

I'm still not quite sure what that was all about, but she subsequently reported a tremendous increase in intuition, being able to start crystal divining, and her dowsing abilities were getting better all the time.

Many of my clients and friends have used EFT to extend their abilities with things as divergent as healing powers, ESP, reading the Tarot better, more rapport with their spirit guides and many other esoteric applications beside.

These extra-sensory endeavours always respond well to releasing traumatic memories relating to the subject (one gentleman "saw" his dead grandmother when he was a small child, remarked upon this to father, who then proceeded to beat him up whilst yelling, "You're going to go mad just like your Uncle Peter if you don't stop this evil right now!").

'Religious' education of one kind and another can also create serious stumbling blocks to contacting intuitive talents later on in life; freeing oneself from fears and traumas relating to this area can and does lead to a gentle flowering of those types of gifts.

EFT & Learning

We have known for a long time that human beings are veritable learning machines. We have more neurons in our brains than there are stars in the visible sky, and the possibility of connections between them are to all intents and purposes, infinite.

I'm sure you've heard it said that we only use 5% of our brains - yet if all of this is true, why do we make such heavy weather of learning new things, of studying, and of using what we have learned?

One answer certainly lies in negative beliefs, forged by negative emotions, in moments of trauma, at some point in our past.

On this subject, here are a three learning related examples:

Dyslexia

I treated a 14 year old girl for dyslexia using EFT. She was so full of limiting beliefs, I kept sighing and shaking my head all through the session. From, "I was born stupid", to "There's nothing I can do right" to, "I must be brain damaged" and anything imaginable in between, this poor girl had no belief left that she could ever achieve anything at all.

Before the treatment she tensed up and turned white when I handed her a piece of paper with the word "horse" written on it. She clutched it so hard that the paper tore and after staring at it, desperately, brow furrowed, she just shook her head and turned it over, handed it back to me face down.

After the treatment, she looked at a new sheet of paper with the word, "horse" written on it once more, and said, "That's an h, right? And an o? Would that be horse?" When I smiled and nodded, she just kept shaking her head and saying over and over, "Horse. That's right. It's horse. I guessed it right."

She is still way, way behind in all her subjects but I cannot begin to tell you how much difference not being terrified of her own failure anymore made to this girl.

This was one of those cases where I had to say, "God Bless EFT" as I closed the door behind her.

Inability To Study

Another teenager was about to take his A level tests, and was in such a state that he made an appointment with a hypnotherapist behind his parent's back - me. He didn't want to be there, but he was absolutely desperate. He couldn't sleep, he tried to study and couldn't concentrate, and "everything is going black all around me." It turned out that a teacher at secondary school had told him that he would never amount to everything and he would be lucky if he got a job on the dustcarts. Ever since, school had become a burden and studying and learning a terrible struggle.

He continued tapping for himself after the session, and passed his A levels with one A grade, and two B's. I got a sweet thank you card from him on which he wrote, "Without your help, I would have killed myself."

Exam Phobia

One young lady, a university student, came to see me because she had no trouble learning but was absolutely petrified during exams. She was entirely incapable of remembering much of anything she had learned and which she knew she knew, but just couldn't get to during an exam. This was terribly frustrating to everyone concerned, not least of all her tutors, because she really should have been in the top five of her classes, but barely passed if she passed at all. Each semester it became more and more nerve racking to find out if her excellent course work would be just enough again to offset her terrible exam results.

We used EFT to uncover the root cause - a simple little memory from school, where she had taken a test, was absolutely certain she had done wonderfully well and had her test returned, marked with a "D". She had been horrified and shocked and at that moment lost all belief in her ability to produce good results on tests.

She told me later, "I tapped and tapped before the next test. I wasn't actually scared of the test anymore, but scared that the fear would come back. When I got the paper with the questions, it was so easy, I couldn't believe it. It was like I was just sitting at home, doing my homework. On one point, I got stuck and couldn't remember a particular study I wanted to quote, so I just tapped right there and then, in the middle of the test, and the answer jumped into my mind. If only I had EFT years ago! How much suffering that would have saved me!"

When I asked her what the score was, she said, "Oh that, yes it was about 94%."

Life Is Learning!

Learning is, of course, not only about school type learning.

EFT can help make it easier, whatever you want to learn or learn to do better - from horse riding, to golf, snooker, bowling, singing, playing a musical instrument, typing, or even in a much wider sense, such as learning to become a more patient parent, a more effective sales person, a better lover. See also examples from "Performance".

But really and if you think about it, learning goes so much further than that.

There's learning about who you are and what you are supposed to be doing with and in your life; there's learning about yourself and what you do.

There's learning about the patterns of life themselves and learning from your mistakes; and learning from your triumphs, too.

Every single day we are challenged in small ways and in big ones to change our minds about something or other, admit some new evidence into our thoughts, face problems and challenges and we need to **learn to solve these** challenges in some way.

It has been my observation that people – all people! – have deep beliefs about what learning is, how useful it is, whether they can do it at all, how easy it is and many more besides.

Learning extends into every area of everything we do – if I could learn to make myself sick with too much work or by abusing my body, can I now learn to do something else instead and make myself well again?

For anyone involved in any form of personal development or healing, basic beliefs about learning may well hold the deep keys to transformation, growth and healing.

EFT & Limitations

What are the things you truly think you cannot do? If you have EFT, you need to think again, because it simply blows limitations out of the water.

I love the story of the two meridian therapists chatting at a conference.

One said, "I'm absolutely petrified of flying. Haven't been in an aircraft for 20 years or more. Ah yes, and I booked myself a holiday the other day, to Spain."

Says the other, "But what of your fear of flying?"

The first therapist laughed. "Oh I'm petrified right now but it's ok, I can always do a bit of EFT – it'll be alright."

I love this story because that's me, too. I was petrified of driving any kind of distance since a bad accident some 15 years ago. Yet when asked to do a 500 mile round trip, I said, "Sure. I can tap all the way if I have to."

As it turned out, I didn't need to tap at all. I was perfectly alright and coped just fine. What amazes me is that I would never have found out that I could do this without EFT – because I wouldn't even have tried!

There is a reason, you see, that we (people who are using EFT in a professional as well as a personal context) are so enthusiastic about it, and that it is far more than "just another technique" to us. Every single one of us has had such experiences of finding ourselves doing things we never thought we possibly could. Doing these things and finding that we could do them easily and that they were fun, even.

Things like climbing high towers, driving long distances, speaking to a group of professionals for two days, cold calling radio stations – all kinds of things.

Perhaps to me the greatest gift of EFT is the trust I have in the technique, and that this trust allows me to go beyond my own pre-conceived limitations.

I deeply and profoundly wish that you will experience the same. It is a wonderful gift of new found freedom and an expansion to your personal horizons.

EFT & "Little Things"

It's amazing when one facilitates and observes wonderful changes in people's health and emotional well-being, how painful memories of 50 years are simply laid to rest and huge, marvellous, life transformational shifts are taking place.

But for me, the true miracle of EFT is what I call the "little things".

Some people choose to use EFT to overcome just one major problem, and then never use it again. Others, like myself, seize upon EFT and apply to everything and everywhere and make it an integral part of their lives.

My friend Marion said, "EFT is a lifeline. I don't know how I ever got through the days without it. I use it for everything that comes my way and upsets me, frightens me, stresses me out. It's impossible to begin to describe how much I've achieved with it, and in how many different areas of my life.

Most of all, it is the knowledge that I have EFT to help me cope with stress and pain that makes it such an essential help to me, an invisible friend on which I can depend to help me and to soothe me, no matter what."

I second this, wholeheartedly. Here are a few personal examples from me and my own life about the "little things", from an article I wrote on the subject for the Association For Meridian Therapies Newsletter:

On Friday, I finally had my new patio doors fitted. On Saturday morning, I smashed them accidentally when I dropped a heavy screwdriver which bounced point first and shattered the glass into a million pieces. I was about to start berating myself for my stupidity when I sat on a chair and tapped instead. And so, I just cleaned it all up and ordered the replacement glass. In the past, this would have spoiled the entire weekend at least and may have even led into a full blown feeling of depression and unhappiness.

Now, it's ok.

There are so many things that used to upset me and that are now ok, too.

Like a condescending bank manager, getting stuck in traffic, getting nervous before appearing in public, being afraid to go to the dentist, losing my temper with my children, looking into the mirror in the morning and deciding I'm no longer beautiful, headaches, worries and indecisions.

Like, I'm in a tight old fashioned English car park, trying to get into a parking spot, with an audience at a bus stop watching me with amused interest as I'm going backwards and forwards and getting ever more uptight and stuck.

I stopped and had a quick tap for "Even though I'm useless at parking cars" and just two minutes later, reversed into the spot easily and with a flourish.

Like, I was tiling the kitchen and trying to cut heavy ceramic tiles. I was shattering four before getting one good cut. Totally exasperated with myself, I finally decided to stop and tap for, "Even though I can't cut tiles to save my life" which calmed me down, so I started again. And found to my amazement that the tile cutter ran across the tiles easily, and the tiles snapped cleanly every time. The only way I can explain this is that I must have been uptight which resulted in a jagged cut, causing the tiles to shatter across the uneven fault line. Once I had tapped and was more relaxed, the cut was straight and clean.

Like, I used to hate washing up. But I did it three times each day or more, always moaning and groaning inwardly and outwardly. Then I finally decided to tap for it. It turned out I hated it so much because my mother used make me wash up in the hotel my parents owned, from about age 5 onwards, and the amounts of dishes were horrendous, virtually never ending. Having laid this particular set of memories to a long deserved rest, I now quite enjoy washing up the comparably miniscule amounts our household produces. I put on a nice tape whilst I do it and find it quite relaxing. Moreover, since I don't think of washing up as a terrible strain and hell-like punishment anymore, I have found I can ask my children to do it on the odd occasion so now I'm only doing it half the time.

All these little annoyances day in, day out. Each one a little grain of sand in my shoe, altogether a big rock that made walking through life so tiring and difficult.

Now, they're going. One by one. And in a funny way, that's contributing more to my daily happiness, serenity and peace of mind than the big transformational shifts I thought I needed to make me happy.

EFT & Long Term Tapping

My friends, family and clients as well as myself have been tapping for about four years now.

There are a number of things we have found out with the wisdom of hindsight, so I will share them with you at the start of your journey.

Most importantly, when you first start to work on issues by yourself, is to engage in some discipline.

Basically, most people sit on a whole mountain of issues, negative conditioning, bad memories and the hurts, slights, pains and rejections of a lifetime, no matter if that lifetime was just 5 short years or 85 long ones.

Most of these many minor and major problems are unconscious or semi conscious, and once you start to tap, they will raise their hands for attention and to try and get you to do the next round for them.

One lady told me only this morning that upon receipt of my telephone consultation chart the day before, she had started to tap right away and without waiting for further instructions.

She sat all morning, going from one issue to the other, quite overwhelmed at the magnitude of it all and ended up feeling very strange and went to sleep for the rest of the day and most of the night.

I'm sure that everyone who uses EFT regularly has a story like that to tell.

You start with any old issue, and whilst you're tapping on that, another one turns up and that leads to yet another and so on. This is tempting and also often extremely interesting as you learn how and why your various problems are linked and are created by one another, but it actually doesn't really resolve anything much - it just takes the edge of each issue.

To give an example, if you have a toothache, a headache and a stomach ache, and they're all equally intense, and you begin tapping on the toothache, as soon as this is reduced even slightly, it will of course fade into the background and the other two pains become more urgent and important in your mind. If at that point you turn your attention to the others and tap them both in turn, you end up with three pains, none of which having been completely resolved but just made slightly more bearable.

Therefore, I would advise you to do the following: when you have decided to tap for something, write down the subject on a card or in a notebook.

No matter what happens during the session, keep with this one issue until it has been completely resolved. Say to all the other thoughts that are trying to crowd in, "Look I understand that you're queuing to be healed and that you can't wait to have your emotional intensity released. But let me finish with this one first; when it's your turn, you'll be wanting my undivided attention too."

You can make a note of the other issues arising after each round to make sure you will address them later; but trust me, you'll save a lot of time using this approach in the long run.

One thing that we have found after three years of EFT is that we seem to have more courage in general. I think this is due to the fact that we know we could tap if we needed to and this extra confidence allows us to do more, try more, challenge ourselves more than we previously did.

I think I can speak for my colleagues here when I say that we still use the technique in moments of crisis – yes, we still have those, we are not floating all day in perfect enlightenment yet! – and that the technique has become an integral part of our own lives, regardless of whether we are using EFT with others or not.

For me, at least, this is a real proof of the reality of EFT. I have learned so many techniques, so many different healing modalities over the last 25 years. It is this one I am still turning to as a first choice emergency treatment under any given condition.

EFT & Louise Hay

In view of how helpful many of my clients have found this combination, I would offer it to you.

Louise Hay is an American lady who healed herself of cancer (which she believed to be a manifestation of a mental attitude of holding on to mental scars and memories of pain and injuries in a physical form) by re-examining her attitudes towards herself and changing them with the help of affirmations. She then went on to treat others with often amazing results. What she discovered from this, she now teaches in books and workshops. She is a multi-million selling author.

If you are not familiar with mind-body connections, especially in the realm of finding underlying emotional causes for physical diseases, I would recommend you acquire a copy of Louise Hay's "Heal Your Body" (also known as "The Little Blue Book").

This book lists physical ailments in alphabetical form, then suggests possible underlying emotional causes which have caused the physical ailment to manifest.

Lastly, it suggests an affirmation to help overcome the emotional problem.

Here is an example:

Physical Problem:
Incontinence
Suggested Emotional Root Cause:
Emotional Overflow. Years Of Controlling Emotions.
Suggested Affirmations:
I am willing to feel. It is safe for me to express my emotions. I love myself.

These healing affirmations are a great suggestion to use with EFT treatments, either in the way they are, or in their reverse form turned into an opening statement:

"Even though I'm not willing to feel, I deeply and profoundly accept myself ..."
"Even though I don't think it's safe to express my emotions, ..."
"Even though I don't love myself, ..."

These can serve either as the starting point to help uncover personal root causes or to simply start alleviating the problem all by themselves.

Here's another example, this time with a real life person:

I saw a teenage boy called Jason because he had been stealing things. He also suffered from nose bleeds which had become very frequent at the same time he started his stealing spree, which in itself had begun about 6 months after a new baby brother by a new step father had arrived in the family.

He was entirely unaware of the (to me most obvious) connection between these events, so I gave him the little blue book and had him read out loud what it said about nosebleeds:

Physical Problem:
Nosebleeds
Emotional Root Causes:
A need for recognition.
Feeling unrecognised and unnoticed. Crying out for love.
Affirmations:
I love and approve of myself.
I recognise my own self worth.
I am wonderful.

After having him tap a round for, "Even though I am totally not wonderful" (his choice of words!), he became very thoughtful and offered the insight that although he wasn't perfect, he was perhaps not as bad as he sometimes thought he was. Following him taking away slight variations on the Louise Hay affirmations to tap every day by the way of homework, his nosebleeds have stopped and not returned.

Using EFT in this way and in conjunction with the suggestions in the blue book, you can both undo the underlying trauma and then use the affirmations in a positive way for the healing effects - a most powerful combination indeed and easy to apply, even if you are not a professional therapist.

EFT & Love Pain

In the course of an average person's life, there is very little that can cause such extreme emotions, trauma and upset than what happens around the subject of romantic love.

You, dear reader, might have forgotten what it was like once upon a time, to be in a state where nothing else but the other and what they thought, did and said seemed to matter; the heartbreak (metaphorically and literally) of rejection, the bereavement of desertion, the agony of trust and love betrayed.

I have worked with many people suffering from the fallout of what is called "love pain" - some of it brand new and current; in one particular case nearly 70 years old yet still as painful and raw as it had been all those years ago. I have also known many others for whom all the healing, meditating and forgiving in the world had done little or nothing to reduce these super intense emotions to anything resembling a bearable level - that is, until the arrival of EFT.

EFT has no philosophy, it has no religion and it doesn't demand we change or learn any lessons. It simply allows us to release pain - any kind of pain, may this be as the result of an undeserved accidental trauma or the pain resulting from decisions we made.

Love Pain, its related traumas and resulting decisions, can and do have long lasting repercussions on all kinds of areas in a person's life. These hurts permeate any kind of relationship, they lurk behind all kinds of anxieties and beliefs about how worthwhile you are, they can even rub off on children brought up by a person who carries such shadows through their lives.

I have assisted many in releasing such pain these past 12 months and the difference it has made to their lives is awe-inspiring. Whether you need to or wish to apply EFT in this area of your life, I'm sure you will find it a most deeply healing experience that can go a long way to open up your potential to be a more happy, more fulfilled and more loving person.

EFT & Metaphors

In my opinion, metaphors or "mental pictures and movies", are the language of the unconscious mind.

Metaphors kick in when we try to describe something and ordinary words begin to fail us

- my love for him was like a tidal wave;
- the pounding in my head was like a thousand sledgehammers;
- my fear was like I was drowning in a dark ocean;
- this addiction is my personal demon;
- my life is a wasteland.

Whether it is therapeutic metaphor elicitation you're after, interpreting your dreams, or even finding a representation to be the new logo for your company's stationary, EFT can be used most creatively and most successfully to change metaphors, to move them along, and to discover their relevance and meaning.

I recently saw a client whose original problem was resolved very quickly indeed - it was a phobia of rats that went away entirely after one single round of tapping. I had arranged for the presence of a pet rat so the test concluded positively and we had time on our hands. Whilst chatting she told me she often dreamed that she was a slug or a snail, and in her dreams would venture forth and then get killed by strong sunlight, or even by giant people sprinkling salt on her back.

I thought that was most fascinating and asked her to tap for, "Even though I'm a slug" just for fun. She laughed at first as she tapped for it, but then fell silent as the round progressed. At the end of the round, she told me, "I realised all of a sudden what it meant. You know when you see a snail, and it has its feelers out? And then you touch them ever so lightly and they just draw in? Well that's me really. I'm so oversensitive, I just curl up within myself at the slightest little prospect of criticism or rejection."

A friend of mine had been given a very expensive original painting for her wedding anniversary. It depicted a sunset over a lake, and a rowing boat moving towards the far shore where the shadows from the hills lay. She didn't like the picture but felt she had to keep it as she had no good reason to tell her husband to get rid of it. She decided to tap for, "Even though I don't know why I dislike the picture so much" and it turned out that it reminded her of her father's death (the ferryboat into the shadows) and that she would therefore experience a sense of sadness and depression each time she looked at it.

This realisation allowed her to open up a subject matter she had never thought to explore, and after tapping herself for all manner of sad and unhappy emotions relating to her relationship with his father, the picture was no longer a problem and she began to admire it for it's artistic and visionary qualities.

Metaphorical representations can be used very nicely when dealing with both emotional and physical pain that is difficult to describe in any other way. For example, someone might explain their "sadness" to you as "this heavy weight on my chest".

After a round of tapping, you can ask if it has become smaller, lighter, and use this way of making the invisible visible both as excellent opening statements as well as a good test to see how something has changed before and after the treatment.

EFT & Money

In the context of success coaching, I have been struck over and over again by the sheer contortions about money that exist in virtually everybody's mind.

As I have no experience with clients complaining of having too much money and suffering from sleepless nights because they simply don't know how to spend it all, I think we'll just go right ahead and look at some strategies on how to overcome money problems with EFT.

Since "money" is such a deeply convoluted subject with aspects arising all over the place, a nice idea is to go back to basics. Especially if there are serious money problems, it can be most helpful to start by treating money like you would treat a spider phobia.

Find (or borrow) a banknote of a reasonably large denomination and simply place it in front of you on a desk or table. What springs to mind? What emotions do you feel when you look at it? When I've tested this procedure with people, it was most interesting to note what a variety of negative responses occurred. From, "I don't believe this is mine", via "I don't deserve to have this", to "There's no point getting attached to it, someone will just come and take it away anyhow" - a whole range of depressing, unhappy, and generally truly negative responses were present when you simply confronted an every day adult with a bank note.

This became even more pronounced when I picked up the note, held it out to the person and said loudly, "Here you go, (name), this is for you." Not a single one of my "success coaching" clients could take the money without feeling seriously bad for a whole range of complicated reasons!

The format was just to keep tapping and testing each time by bringing out the bank note again until there was no negative response left and the person took the note happily, readily, and even with a smile in some cases.

If you are intending to do some "money work" by yourself or with friends, use the following as "triggers" (like the spider would be to the spider phobic) to find the aspects of the problem:

- Single bank notes of various denominations
- a pile of banknotes (boy that is a set of interesting aspects!)
- a single large coin (this brings out childhood memories)
- a pile of coins (this brings out childhood memories relating to savings)

Then, we can go on to clear other money related aspects by using some of the following in the same, straightforward way (which is always: trigger, test, tap, trigger, test):

- o bank statements (serial spending and saving habits)
- o payslips/wage packets (apart from career issues, this brings out family/father issues from childhood)
- o credit cards (imagine me laughing here – talk about negative emotions coming to the fore!)
- o credit card statements (which have different aspects to the actual plastic card)
- o building society books, share certificates, or any other paper representation of money that features large in the individual person's life
- o bills and invoices (and especially the red variety)

Financial limits are wonderfully explored by using a friend and both their chequebook and yours. Write each other cheques for ever increasing sums of money and hand them to each other. This can bring out not only the pain of accepting large sums of money, but conversely also the pain of letting go!

- "Money constipation" is just as damaging to a healthy financial system as is
- "money diahorrhea" (where you don't earn but keep on spending regardless),
- "money anorexia" (where you neither earn nor spend) or
- "money bulimia" (where you earn but spend immediately so there's no noticeable gain at the end of the day).

Lastly (and this is a personal favourite of mine), we have what I call "potential money" such as lottery tickets, gambling slips and scratch cards. Entwined in these you will find issues around luck, deservability, and, most interesting of all, often a belief that "this is the **ONLY HOPE** I could possibly have to ever become really rich".*

*__A note__: *Tapping away negative feelings on lottery tickets does not turn someone into a compulsive gambler. On the contrary. It can actually help with compulsive gambling to dis-engage emotion from the trigger the lottery tickets and also game shows, horse races and so on, provide.*

You might think as you read this, "That's a lot of tapping!" but don't fret.

It only seems that way because I have made a list of relevant "money triggers" that in reality covered a whole lot of real people and all their combined problems.

Generally, only some of the triggers reveal the driving forces to a person's overall money problems, and when they have been dealt with, it's not necessary to do all the other ones.

I have mentioned them all so that you could work your way through them over a period of, say, a week.

I promise you, it would truly change your relationship with "money" for the better.

Money As A Symbol For Energy Exchanges

For some people, money isn't just money but actually a symbol for their general "energy exchanges with the environment".

What I mean by this is that the way money behaves for such a person is more or less exactly the same as how for example, relationship exchanges are handled – "I put so much into my relationships but I don't get anything back in return." is just the same for such a person as, "I put so much hard work into my business but I don't see my bank balance increase at the end of the day."

Here, it's not really a money problem but a **general problem with the give and take of energy exchanges** all around, being in a comfortable ebb and flow of giving and taking, receiving and letting go.

This is related in a deep and structural way with survival issues and beliefs and learnings about what it takes to survive at all in this world – all this is an energy exchange, from taking one breath after the other to eating the next meal, to relationships and in the end, to money.

For some people, money problems cannot shift until they have come to some sort of peace arrangement with the processes of life itself and start to begin to be willing and believe that they are able to create their own survival.

Money & Healers

There isn't a single group in society that has such global problems with money as holistic people and especially, holistic healers and those on the path to becoming holistic healers.

I have wondered about this and observed this for many more years and in many more excellent people than one would ever wish to; and one day I had a breakthrough insight on the problem.

In metaphysical work of all kind, there is a 0 balance point where everything is a beautiful balance, in peace and stillness, in total potentiality, in absolute freedom – a state of bliss and of perfection.

It is the point of perfect balance and in metaphysical work, it is indeed most desirable. However, there arises a planes confusion whereby this deep hunger for the perfection of the 0 balance state starts to creep into "every day affairs" such as bank statements.

Neither a lender nor a borrower be – accountants sigh with pleasure when the balance is at the end of the day, at 0 – the books are perfectly balanced.

But in real living and especially with money, 0 is not a place to stay for any length of time. If you had 0 air, 0 food and 0 water, how long would you be able to remain in that state? If you have 0 in your bank account, how will you pay your bills or have the freedom to choose what you want in your life?

Life is FLUX, it moves through phases and cyclic spirals, it never stops and it never sleeps.

EFT self treatments can help you get back into the "flow of things" and it also can help reduce or even completely eliminate the deep feelings of longing and of homesickness for that 0 Balance state that we might well remember from another time or state of being and which, of course, we will achieve again quite naturally, quite automatically and quite without any further ado when our lives have been completed.

Money – Conclusion

I hope this section has sparked some ideas for you where you might begin to use the power of EFT to help you with your own topics and personal challenges with this interesting topic of "money".

EFT & Muscle Testing

Especially in cases where psychological reversal plays a major part, muscle testing of one kind or another can be very helpful. For example, if a person holds out their arm to the side, palm of the hand turned down, and you push on the arm lightly with two fingers, you will feel a certain amount of normal resistance. If reversal is present, the arm will be weaker when the person says a statement relating to the problem in hand - "I want to be healthy".

Some therapists routinely use muscle testing to show reversal to their clients in this way, which can be most useful, especially with clients who won't/can't believe that there are unconscious parts or even their own energy system running a contrary strategy to what they desire so strongly in consciousness.

It can also be used to check when reversal has been eliminated; the person should test strong on "I want to be healthy" and weak on "I want to be sick".

An individual working by themselves can use auto-motor movements instead of muscle testing using a pendulum for example, which would give a yes/no response instead of testing strong or weak, respectively.

EFT & NLP

As a neuro-semanticist and NLP trainer, I have found EFT & NLP to be simply a winning combination.

NLP practitioners are rigorously trained to observe physiological shifts in their clients and to note the language the clients use with great care; when it comes to choosing opening statements, creating and tracking energy shifts in the client's systems, this is of course of great help.

On the other hand, EFTs ability to rapidly release emotions and to undo limiting and negative beliefs is a perfect tool to use in the context of NLP interventions. You can make and test submodality shifts, metaphor work, unconscious installations, and some interventions such as values elicitations, parts integrations and timeline work of any kind can be made both faster and more thorough by the use of EFT.

Another aspect is the trance inducing abilities of EFT without the need to ever mention hypnosis by name; in combination with the languaging and general structure of a typical NLP style intervention, I can only recommend any NLP practitioner to start adding it to their tool box of techniques as soon as possible.

There's one more aspect to NLP and EFT - anyone studying NLP at this time can of course use EFT to make the process of learning it quicker and more thorough by far. I've known friends of mine to tap for such things as, "Even though the meta model is driving me crazy" - "Even though I can't get my head around DHE", "Even though I can't make visual internal representations clearly" - "I want to get more elegant/intuitive in my languaging" - "Even though I can't generate Sleight Of Mouth Patterns" and a hundred and one more issues besides that arise in the study of this particular field.

As NLP is one of my specialties, I have written a special report for fellow neuro-linguists that covers combining NLP & EFT, available from http://starfields.org

EFT & Parts

Whenever there is a great deal of internal conflict, struggle and misery in someone's mind, I tend to think along the lines of "parts".

There are many different names for these little subpersonalities in our minds, such as "the child within", "parent/child/adult" from TA, "neural nets running divergent strategies" etc. but at the end of the day, it is a widespread notion that there are parts of us that don't always agree with other parts of us.

I have personally found EFT absolutely invaluable in resolving parts conflicts, and the easiest way to identify unconscious parts is to use willpower as the yardstick - if you can do something really easily and without a "second thought", you're congruent within yourself and all is well.

If, on the other hand, you have to struggle with yourself to do something or have to "force yourself" with willpower, that means by definition there's a part of you that is opposed to the whole endeavour.

A salesman who desperately wants to phone a potential client, for example, but has to force himself to pick the telephone, has a part that doesn't want him to do so. EFT allows us to speak directly to the part in question, and to relieve this part of its fears, angers and generally, its reasons to stop the man from making that call.

By tapping, "Even though there's a part of me that (has this problem/still hasn't forgiven her/doesn't want me to lose weight/can't stand the thought of having sex/ etc., etc.)" conflicts, internal wars and general misery can be changed into single minded achievement.

This is a good way of dealing with any thoughts, patterns of behaviours and states of being that one individual no longer wants in their lives, or that are no longer a true reflection of who they have become. *See Also Conflict, Relationships, Willpower.*

EFT & Past Lives

Past Life Regression is a very popular and potentially very powerful change and release technique. One reason why people are often rightfully afraid of trying it out is because they are afraid of what they might find, and are unsure as to whether they can cope with the emotions which can be contacted spontaneously during a past life regression treatment.

EFT releases past life emotions as powerfully as it does "real life" emotions, and I have found that by using EFT with traumatic past life memories in exactly the same way as one would use them with current memories, most healing and revealing resolutions can be achieved.

One of my clients brought up, rather shamefacedly, a past life concern which had been haunting her for a number of years. It revolved around being burned at the stake in medieval times. She had acquired this as a result of a session with an untrained practitioner who had failed to resolve the accessed past life with her in a cohesive manner.

Whether one believes in past lives or not, the fact remained that this lady was showing the classical signs of Post Traumatic Stress Disorder - nightmares, pre-occupation with the subject, frequent headaches, skin rashes and depression. Further, once she started to talk about the past life memories, her body showed clearly that there was tremendous emotional charge behind her words - her breathing became shallow, irregular and fast, she began to tremble and sweat, and it was very difficult for her to talk.

We cleaned up the memory using the story approach to find all the aspects, and the lady in question had in the course of the next hour, many new learnings from the past life memory.

By the time we were done, it had released its hold on her entirely.

EFT & Performance

In our culture, it is generally held that in order to maximise one's performance in any area, be it in bed, at school, at work or at play, a lot of hard work is required and endless drill and practise.

I used to subscribe to this notion - until I had a number of interesting experiences with EFT, that is.

The first was a gentleman who called me for hypnotic assistance with speed reading. I asked why he required this, and he told me he had to do a course at work in order to keep his job. He found studying hard, painful and couldn't retain what he was so painfully trying to bash into his brain through his tired eyes night after weary night.

I used EFT to clear numerous limiting beliefs, such as "I am not smart enough", "Reading is difficult", "I can't remember" and so on and then gave him a veritable tome (a huge big book called The Spirit Of Mathematics) and asked him to test himself. He opened it without hesitation, started reading. Stopped. Looked at me in amazement, then down at the book again. "This is unbelievable," he said. "This is so easy? It kind of makes sense? As though the language in the book has changed somehow?"

I have heard this kind of statement in many different guises numerous times since. Once blockages and fears and conscious and unconscious concerns have been resolved, it seems that the mind is then open to just get on and do its own thing - quite without any need for further drilling or practise.

Here are a four more examples of the same kind:

- A young man who learned to play guitar in just 6 weeks. What that means is that at the end of the 6 weeks, he could play and remember virtually any kind of chord, no matter how outlandish the finger placements; he could play single and classical note pieces at their intended speed; he could replicate rhythm patterns after a single listening. He used tapping to

134

undo every limiting thought that came up about how hard this was, or how others couldn't do it either, or how he didn't have any natural talent. His teacher was awestruck and has been sending me clients ever since.

- A lady who had a fear of computer programmes. Once she had finished tapping, she said that when she looked back at the screen, it had changed somehow and instead of undecipherable nonsense hieroglyphics there were just simple file folders and a status bar - perfectly straightforward and easy to learn how to deal with.

- A lady who dropped a white headed thumbtack on a huge pebbled drive. She spent half an hour looking for it, trying to work out where it was, with no success. One round of tapping, and "it just jumped out at me - amongst all those white pebbles. It is unbelievable that I could have made such a fine distinction. It makes me wonder what else my brain could do for me."

- Look also at the examples in the "sports" section.

In all those cases, it wasn't further practise or working harder that was required but simply for us to get out of our own way. I'm still wondering every day what other simple, basic abilities there are waiting for us to call upon them.

I would therefore recommend, whatever the area of performance is that you are interested in expanding, to use EFT first to remove any unnecessary baggage that is holding you back.

In seven out of ten cases, there's really nothing more you need to do to supercharge your performance. Sometimes, there are extra skills that you need to acquire but as I said before, I'm astonished to find how rarely that is actually necessary.

135

EFT & Personal Development

As one cynic once remarked, "Personal Development is the ongoing admission that there's something terribly wrong with you!" One of the greatest gifts of using EFT in my opinion is the ability to release long held, life long, long standing negative beliefs about the self, and about how the world works.

It is remarkable what kind of negativity is to be found in most people once they start looking. I've had more people than I care to remember say with deep conviction that they were evil, doomed, damned, Satan's spawn, bad through and through, useless, hopeless, a waste of space, a terrible person, and any variation on the theme you might like to contemplate.

It is even more remarkable when you consider that I don't generally work with prison inmates or mental patients but with intelligent, enlightened and dedicated "Personal Developers" and many are counsellors, healers, health workers and practitioners in their own right.

A neat way to work with such issues is to take a VOC reading on any kind of issue that you might think of "developing" yourself further.

VOC stands for Validity Of Cognition - on a scale of 10 to 0, 10 being absolutely true and 0 being absolutely false, how true are these statements for you?

You can test yourself on any of your favourite affirmations, such as:

- **I am happy**
- **I am whole**
- **I am abundant**
- **I am healthy**
- **I am a child of the universe**
- **I love myself**
- **I approve of myself**
- **I am loved etc.**

Ask yourself how true you think any given statement is for you, right here, right now.

Accept the first number that comes to mind, and this is the rule of thumb:

- If it's under five, you won't be/have it/get it EVER until you change your mind first.

- If it's above 8, you'll get it/have it/become it very quickly;

- If it's a ten, then you should have it/be it already - if you answered ten and you don't have it, you're deluding yourself or there's a part of you that has a vested interest in keeping you thinking that you believe this when it actually isn't true.

- Between 5 and 7, you'll get there eventually but it will not be as easy or straightforward as it could become.

- If more than one number springs to mind you've got a parts conflict on the subject and you need to deal with each number separately.

Don't worry about finding out that your internal views on many subjects are far from fully enlightened as you believed them to be/would have hoped them to be. EFT can help you align your unconscious beliefs and let go of negative conditioning.

As an example, if you take the statement, "I am happy", and, as you say it, you feel it's not really true, about a 3 at best, you can tap for, "Even though I'm not happy, I deeply and profoundly accept myself" and see where this leads you - to memories, decisions, traumas, whatever; use EFT to resolve what you have found and then, ask yourself the question again.

This time, **the number should have changed and be considerably higher.**

You can then go on to decide if you wish to leave it there for now or go for a full score of 10 with further tapping, such as, "I want to remove all blocks to my ability to be happy ..."

Sometimes, it's helpful to say, "Even though there's a part of me (that doesn't believe I am loved, deserve to be happy, I'm a child of the universe)" to unearth any objections or reasons you might have had in the past.

If this sounds like too much hard work, you can just tap for, "I want to be happy and I fully and completely accept myself" a number of times a day and leave it at that, checking with the VOC scale every so often. This approach is particularly useful if you have a notion that you might be psychologically reversed on the subject of "happiness".

If you, like myself, have a good collection of Nightingale Conant type tape sets of inspirational and motivational speakers which might not have brought forth the improvements you had hoped they would when you purchased them, I suggest you re-visit with these tape sets and use them in the following way:

Listen carefully to the speaker. As soon as they make a statement and you feel internal resistance/negative emotions/negative thoughts/

depression setting in, stop the tape and tap right away for the issue that was thus revealed. Then continue with the programme.

An average 6 tape set will probably take you a week or so to get through if you spend an hour a day on this, but by the end of your own special course in personal development, you probably will be in a mental position to actually make good use of what the motivational speaker suggested.

I highly recommend this!

EFT & Pets

In the section on Children, I mentioned briefly the idea of surrogate or proxy tapping. As I have numerous pets of my own, I took notice of people using EFT with their pets, to alleviate behaviour problems, health problems, training problems, and all manner of relationship based problems, too. I found this particularly fascinating because pets can't partake in "placebo effects" - if the owner taps on themselves and the pet two rooms away changes it's behaviour or stops limping, it tells me that there is a very powerful energetic shift taking place.

Here's just one of the many pet tapping stories that have come across my path; even if you do not own pets, think of how useful a method this could be in the context of human problems.

Bobby & The Hot Air Balloon

By Marilyn Pawson

"I have a seven year old poodle cross named Bobby. He's very stable and very obedient, but two days ago, when we out for a walk, a hot air · balloon lost height and descended right on top of us. Bobby panicked completely - I have never seen him like this.

He tore away, would not listen to me and just ran and ran. I tried to go after him but lost him a few miles later, seeing him streaking away in a blind panic across a field and out of sight.

My husband and I searched everywhere for him but couldn't find him, so we went home. About 5 hours later, he returned. He was in a terrible state.

He was trembling, his pupils totally dilated, shivering, twitching, and panting. I gave him some Arnica and Rescue Remedy and sat with him but he wasn't taking any notice of me, he just lay in his bed like in a coma. We went to bed, and I was hoping he'd be better in the morning, but he was just the same and I was now really frightened for him. So I sat down by his bed and started tapping myself for, "Even though Bobby was absolutely terrified by that hot air balloon, I deeply and profoundly love and accept him".

Half way through the round, I felt a shiver go over my back. At the exact same time, Bobby stood up in his bed, stretched, yawned, then shook and started wagging his tail and came over to lick me. He was back.

I put him out in the garden and he was absolutely fine - no shaking, he didn't even look up at the sky. The same morning he even dug up a bone which he hasn't done since he was a puppy. This was an amazing experience for me. I don't know what I would have done without the tapping."

There is a dedicated group for pet owners using meridian therapies with their companions, both by tapping them directly and tapping them by proxy, which also is engaged in research to create a framework for easy-to-apply strategies any pet owner can learn to use.

Further Information on Animal Healing with Energy Therapies:

- The Animal EFT website is at: http://animalEFT.org

- The Energy Therapies For Companions News Group List Home is at: http://yahoogroups.com/group/etcompanions

- For anyone who is serious about Energy Healing For Animals, I have written a very special course which can be found on http://starfields.org

- Understanding and healing behaviour problems in animals – http://a1harmony.com

EFT & Phobias

Phobias are what the meridian energy based therapies were originally invented for. They are high end, completely irrational fears that throw the owner of such fears into a state of blind panic in the presence of a stimulus which triggers the parts of their mind where the phobia is stored.

Dare I say that a really good phobia is one of my favourite things to be able to cure with EFT? It is just so great to see a person do things they could never have contemplated in their wildest dreams; to see their responses of joy and utter amazement; to hear them tell you how this will change their lives for the better.

I also like phobias because the owners do not need any further convincing as to how wonderful EFT is. When I was conducting introduction workshops, I would ask each person to bring a negative emotion they don't need anymore; and I generally would not accept anything that is below a 6 on the SUDs level rating. The reason for this is that it's too easy to explain the shift away afterwards and not attribute it where it rightfully belongs (see also Apex Problem in Chapter 3).

If you are treating yourself for a phobia, look carefully at the agoraphobia example in "EFT & Willpower"; and you might also find it useful to treat yourself for "The fear of the fear" which is for many who have suffered with phobic responses for a long time, nearly as intense a fear as the phobia itself.

If the phobic response to the "trigger" (as the spider would be to the spider phobic) is extreme, it is advised for the client's safety to start by approaching this problem with a lot of distance, both physically as well as mentally.

For example, a treatment for a super intense fear of rats (I seriously thought the client was going to have a heart attack at the mere mention of the word) had the following steps to it to make it as painless as possible: first, we tapped whilst the client was thinking about rats.

When this no longer created a phobic response, we went on to tapping with a picture of a rat at a safe distance away, face down on the opposite side of the room.

Two rounds of tapping later, and the person in question could walk across the room and pick up the paper and turn it over.

More aspects emerged, and only when the person was congruently happy with the picture of the rat was the thought introduced to see a real life rat in a pet shop.

EFT & Primary Gain

Every cloud has a silver lining, and every problem has its upside somewhere, too.

Psychology uses the term "Secondary Gain" for this well known phenomenon. In some cases, the benefits of having the problem are so great, they outweigh the suffering the problem is causing; in some cases, these benefits turn out to be the reason for acquiring the problem in the first place (I call that the Primary Gain and reserve the term Secondary Gain for the lemonade someone learns to make from the lemons their lives created).

Let's state something right up front about this phenomenon because it is important to understand that "creating" a problem unconsciously is not a sign of being a hypochondriac, or being weak or feeble in some way. In the contrary, this "problem creation" happens mostly with people who are far too hard on themselves and keep on forcing themselves into certain ways of living or behaviours that are toxic, damaging and dangerous.

Eventually, their unconscious mind will come up with a way to get them a better deal – even if it means creating an illness or a psychological problem that is not under their control.

Here are three examples where the "Primary Gain" had to be addressed first for the problem to be allowed to leave:

A retired lady with kidney pains.
She had had the most extensive allopathic testing, treatments and even exploratory surgery but "there was nothing physically wrong with her".

In spite of there not being anything wrong with her, the pain she experienced was very real and ever present. The pain didn't move when we tapped, either, so I asked what the benefits of the pain were and how her life had changed since the pain arrived.

She told me that her husband had for the first time since they'd been married in 1942 started to take over some of the housework; that he was much more considerate and would help her with the shopping and do all the heavy cleaning now; and that her two daughters no longer brought all their respective children to be looked after.

When we talked and tapped some more, it was that last issue that had "caused" the pain to appear – she did not feel that she could tell her daughters that the children were simply too much for her now, and not to have to look after the babies especially was a total relief.

We tapped on "Even though I should look after the babies" and "I can't tell them I don't want to help them". She reflected for a while afterwards and said that she had done her child rearing and that she would be able to set boundaries with her daughters in future. Then, we tapped on the pain again. It receded noticeably, but there was a remnant of 3 which remained stuck.

We tapped on, "Even though I can't expect my husband to help me out if I'm not in pain" until the lady felt that she could expect this, and could ask for his help, and that he would probably give it gladly. We went back to the remaining pain, and this time it went down to 0 in a single round.

In this case, the extra attention from the husband was the secondary gain (icing on the cake or the lemonade), and the babysitting the primary gain (the reason for having manifested the problem).

144

A long standing weight problem.

This lady had a long standing weight problem and although EFT had helped her with other things, it "did not seem to work for the weight issue". When we talked about the benefits of having the problem, for a while she wouldn't believe that there could possibly be anything good about being seriously fat whatsoever. But after a while, she hesitantly offered the following:

- she didn't have to go to work or go outside much which was stressful and frightening to her;

- she was "out of the competition" with other women, a competition she felt she could never win, even when she was slim, because "she was so ugly".

- her husband had stopped making sexual demands on her;

- she felt more in control of her body and her life than she had ever felt when she was slimmer.

I helped her resolve these issues and their respective aspects and memories; much of the tapping was done by herself at home.

After two weeks, she felt ready to begin to address the weight issue itself and found it possible now to deal with the practical aspects (such as hunger pangs, cravings for certain foods, buying too many unsuitable foods when in the supermarket, and fear of exercise) with focus and essentially, all by herself.

Not just pretending ...

Remember when you're dealing with primary and secondary gain to ask the question, "What could be the reason/s for wanting or needing to keep this problem in place?"

In this next example, the answer was surprisingly simple, and it unblocked the route for EFT to work its magic once again.

This gentleman had suffered from a stroke, which left the right side of his body paralysed. He had had much physiotherapy and could now move his arm a tiny bit, and said he wanted to try EFT to be able to regain more movement.

When nothing seemed to happen after a single round, he sighed and said, "Oh well that was that then. At least I've tried it."

I found it a little puzzling that he would "give up" so readily when I had heard how much perseverance he had put into his physiotherapy, so I asked him, "What would happen if it worked like a charm and you could regain full movement of your arm, and your leg as well?"

He looked at me in horror and exclaimed, "Why, then everyone would know I was a fraud and that I'd just put it on all these months!"

It turned out that he had so much in the way of examinations, second opinions, and insurance doctors coming in and, at least in his mind, "suggesting that he was faking it to get early retirement", that he had a terrible fear of waking up and finding the problem gone, and being publicly unmasked as a hypochondriac, a liar and a cheat.

In his case, his unconscious mind needed to be assured of two things: firstly, that he would never have to go back to work again which had been unbearably stressful (and I have the notion, this had directly caused the stroke in the first place); and secondly, that people CAN get better WITHOUT it meaning that they are hypochondriacs, liars and cheats. Once these fears had been allayed, the tapping produced a very noticeable increase in his ability to move and control his arm, and he was also able to stand up and take a couple of steps with my support.

He continued to tap, and the physiotherapy progressed very smoothly from that day on. Last I heard, he has recovered 80% of his movements. He is still tapping every day.

To sum up this section: the gains, and especially the primary gains, i.e. the reason for having any kind of problem, are extremely important. At any time you are stuck with a problem you are working on, considering what gains there could be and addressing this first can make all the difference to the outcomes.

EFT & Problem People

"Do you know," said a friend of mine over coffee the other day, "I swear I'd still be married if I had learned EFT two years ago."

This is an interesting statement on many levels, mostly because although she said it offhand, we both knew that it was absolutely correct. She had left her husband mostly because being with him made her feel bad most of the time. If she'd had EFT, she could have tapped these feelings away; or rather, she could have tapped the issues away that had resulted in her feeling bad.

Is this a good thing or a bad thing? I personally believe, as I've already said before, that we're not in this world to suffer, at least not non-stop and without let up for long periods of time. It's far too enchanting, mysterious and beautiful.

Suffering and especially ongoing suffering as opposed to the kind of pain the zebra feels as the lion breaks its neck, seems to be a human pre-occupation. Take away the underlying states of continuous suffering and the mind runs sweet and clear and all kinds of creative solutions to problems may be found.

In situations involving people problems, or relationship problems of any kind, there are two things one can do to regain a balanced state of mind pretty much instantly. The first is the direct approach, i.e. just tapping for the basic problem "as is" - "Even though James drives me insane with his never-ending whingeing, I deeply and profoundly accept myself." for example. This should make you feel a whole lot better, right away.

Then there is another, more in-depth approach which is related to proxy tapping: "Even though James drives me insane with his never-ending whingeing, I deeply and profoundly love and accept James."

147

This is a profoundly powerful statement which has wide ranging repercussions not only for your own neurology, but possibly also for the person who is named as being loved and accepted in spite of their shortcomings or trespasses.

In cases where the suffering at the hands of another person has been long standing, extreme or both, sometimes people cannot bring such a statement over their lips, although at the conscious level they realise that this would probably go a long way towards resolving the existing conflict with the person in question. A good warm up statement would be something along the lines of: "Even though I cannot find it in my heart to love and accept this person, I deeply and profoundly love and accept myself", or "Even though I'm not able to accept this person, I deeply and profoundly love and accept myself."

If you can manage that for a few days, a time might arrive where you feel ready to move on to the next step which is:

"Even though I realise that the problem with James is my problem, I deeply and profoundly accept myself"

... based on the idea that you cannot change another, you can only change yourself. This might be enough to resolve the problem altogether; many people have found this type of "reclaiming the power" statement very liberating indeed.

You know you have resolved an issue with a person thoroughly when you can contemplate forgiving them, and then find that there's nothing left to forgive. That's the general test on people problems.

I recommend especially the "Even though this person did X, I deeply and profoundly love and accept this person" statement. It borders on the magical and I have known it to be used to good effect with lovers, children, parents, neighbours, colleges, bosses and business partners.

In each instance, the person who did the tapping ended up feeling released, liberated and far more balanced, happy and able to cope.

148

EFT & Problem Solving

Have you ever noticed that if someone comes to you for advice, it's ever so easy and straightforward to determine right away where they are stuck in their thinking and to find a solution for them?

The reason that this is so is that we're not emotionally involved in the situation; as it isn't our problem, our thinking remains clear, we can access all the resources, knowledge and learnings we have accumulated over the course of a lifetime and so it's easy to come up with a strategy for another that will most likely lead to success.

Here's a different way of explaining the same phenomenon. I'm sure you are familiar with this strange feeling when you have struggled and worried about something for a long time and eventually the answer comes to you, and you hit your forehead and cry, "Of course! It's so obvious! I can't believe it took me so long to figure it out!"

With EFT, you can have such revelations whenever you want, at your own discretion and without struggling for ages first.

Here are a four examples of how EFT users have applied this:

Advertising Ideas

Sharon was an energy healer and found it very difficult to get new clients other than by referral from her satisfied existing customers. She kept placing advertisements in the local paper but got very little response from them, if any at all. Finally, she sat down and tapped for "Even though I just don't know how to get more clients ..."

Later, she reported, "Within minutes, all kinds of ideas started flooding into my mind. I wrote as fast as I could to note them all down in case they went away again! By the time I had finished, there were over thirty different ideas scribbled on that piece of paper. I applied just the three most obvious ones, and I've got more clients than I can handle now. What gets me is that all of them were so blatantly obvious. What on Earth was I thinking before?"

Smart as Einstein?

Danny got a puzzle reputedly set by Einstein on his e-mail group, together with a challenge to solve it as quickly as possible. Apparently, only 2% of the population could hope to succeed in solving it. After half an hour's struggle, he gave up and tapped for it.

As he says, "It was bizarre. The way to solve it flowed into my mind, like running water. I went back and solved it there and then - and was amongst the first three on the list to get it right!"

Those **** Computers ...!

Alex had a website that simply wouldn't run. He spent four days trying to figure out the problem, re-wrote all of the code a number of times and still it didn't work. Eventually, his girlfriend virtually forced him to tap because she couldn't stand the swearing anymore.

Just one round of tapping and the one little thing became apparent to him that he had overlooked for some reason - namely that the problem might not have been at his end, but with the server. A telephone call later, and the website was up and running.

Terrible Teenager ...?

Petra had terrible problems with her teenage daughter. She had just moved out again and gone to live with a man of some ill repute, and Petra was at her wit's end. So she tapped for, "Even though I don't know what to do with Tracy" and the answer came to her very swiftly - namely, that she had failed to be honest with her daughter, had pretended she had been some kind of vestal virgin when she was her daughter's age which was as far away from the truth as you can get – indeed, she herself had given birth to Tracy when she had been **younger** than her own daughter was now. This one simple thing was lying between them, ever present, like a giant wall. She went to see Tracy within minutes after tapping, and although their relationship is still extremely volatile, Tracy is back at home and, as Petra said, "We are communicating at a whole new and much more productive level."

I could go on and on with examples, but at any point you are stuck in your life with what seems an irresolvable conflict that is completely beyond your ability to cope, try a few rounds of EFT. With the stress and fall out from negative emotions removed, it is far more likely that you will be able to give yourself the sound advice you already have waiting for you inside your own mind.

One last note about problem solving - I have mentioned this before but it is pertinent here to say it again: some problems are such that you cannot resolve them by yourself - they are the equivalent of trying to pull yourself out of a swamp by your own hair. Help from an/another EFT practitioner, or even from a good and trusted friend, can be the only way forward in such cases. I strongly urge you to allow yourself to call upon people in this way if you are stuck with an issue, rather than to think that it is insurmountable.

EFT & Public Performance

I'm sure you've heard it said that the fear of public speaking is quoted as the most intense problem in surveys and that it outranks even fear of death easily.

As a teacher and therapist, there are few changes that delight me as much as when someone who has suffered from this problem finally lays it to rest, goes forth and blossoms into a wonderfully impressive and effective speaker, singer, musician, actor, teacher or presenter.

I think the reason I like this so much is because people who have this particular fear lock up all they know and all they have to give to those who would be delighted and even enlightened by listening to them, and that's such a sad waste on every level!

What I have called fear of public performance comes in many guises.

There's the obvious fear of speaking in front of groups. As a teacher-trainer, I have sat there many times, watching their terrible suffering and their struggles to find words when the mind had gone on strike, the heart was beating too fast, the voice had gone and the hands and forehead were sweating profusely, wanting to take the person in question off the stage and just hold them until they felt better.

There are also many other problems that come into the same category, such as making telephone calls, having people come to visit, or even writing advertisements that will be seen by thousands of people. All of these share aspects of "public performance" or having "an audience that will judge you in some way".

Many people who have learned EFT from me have remarked how comforting it was to know that they would be able to do a little surreptitious tapping at the worst point of the whole thing, i.e. when they were waiting to "come on".

They also told me that it was very rarely necessary at all once the problem had been treated with EFT, but still it was nice to know - just in case!

It is not necessary, once you've used EFT for a while, to go through the whole sandwich routine each time. It is quite sufficient to just rub or touch a spot or two which can be done without anyone who watches being the wiser and in this way, even possible freak outs in mid-performance can be dealt with for effective, on-the-spot relief.

Singing In Public

Myriam said, "I am a singer, and it is ludicrous that I should be afraid of singing in public, but I've always been scared, no, more like, terrified. I used to try alcohol before going on stage, but that wasn't useful or healthy. Since I have had EFT, my singing has become the joy it should have been for years.

"Moreover, should something happen during the performance, such as one of the musicians making a bad mistake, or even hecklers in the audience, all I do is give myself a few taps on the Karate Chop point and I'm right back in this calm, relaxed, 'I can do anything' frame of mind."

This aspect of "enjoying yourself whilst performing" is something else that delights me about using EFT with public performance anxiety.

Not one of the clients I have seen with this particular problem could even conceive of actually "enjoying" it, yet with the fears gone, they did. Further, not only did they enjoy themselves "out in front", as a result their actual performance became much better - more confident, more cohesive, more fluent and the audiences responded in turn.

See also: Speaking Out.

EFT & Reiki

EFT & Reiki, both being energy based forms of healing, naturally combine to produce very powerful results indeed.

About a week ago I was present when a Reiki practitioner treated a client by sending the Reiki energy directly into the tapping points.

The client's responses were amongst the most intensive I have observed, and a single round of combined Reiki/EFT with a Reiki style overall clearing afterwards completely healed a wound this person had been carrying for over 30 years. Another Reiki practitioner told me that every time she started to tap herself or another, automatically her hands would become hot which was her sign that Reiki channelling was taking place.

On the other side of the coin, a Reiki Master told me that they had used EFT to undo a number of blockages to the effectiveness of their own ability to channel healing energy. Apparently, there had been problems in their original training which had caused unhappiness and doubt; once these negative emotions were relieved, the Reiki Master found their abilities taking a quantum leap.

Lastly, EFT interventions can sometimes unbalance a client's energy system temporarily.

Using an all over Reiki re-balancing after an EFT session can make it faster and easier for the client to re-integrate into the new order of things and helps prevent occurrences of the Apex Effect.

EFT & Relationships

At the core and centre of all relationship problems lie strong and overwhelming emotions such as fear, low self esteem, unpleasant emotions such as jealousy, feeling abandoned, feeling hurt, feeling unlovable, feeling trapped, feeling desperate, feeling unloved.

If there weren't any emotions involved, there wouldn't be such a thing as a relationship problem at all - this is important to note and to remember.

After all, if a single man wasn't afraid of rejection and the painful emotions this creates, he could just chat up one woman after another, 40 a night, every night, until one finally said "Yes please!"

If a battered woman wasn't low, depressed, unhappy, scared, and worst of all, probably still in love with the guy in question, she would probably be able to pick up and leave.

So first of all, sit back for a moment and consider what the worst problem are (or the things that cause you to feel the worst, to use different words) and either write it down or make a mental note. I've put the probable corresponding emotions in brackets, but it's the statements that count. Do this now.

Examples could be:

- He is driving me crazy with his womanising (anger!)
- I can't stand her company any more (repulsion, rejection)
- She doesn't even know that I exist (sadness, anger, helplessness)
- I'm sure he's having an affair (fear, terror, anxiety, panic)
- I don't trust her anymore (hurt, anger)
- This relationship is killing me (depression, sadness, fear)
- I can't find anybody to love me (hopelessness, sadness)

- I'm not good enough to be loved (hopelessness)

You can just treat your relationship pains with EFT and all is well. However, you can use it for more than that.

For examples, beliefs such as, "All men are bastards" have a nasty habit of becoming absolutely true for those who believe it, whilst the nice men pair off with the women who believe that "I will find a nice man who loves me and makes me feel wonderful at every street corner!".

Similarly, beliefs such as "Nobody loves me", "I'm too ugly to be lovable", "I'll never find a decent partner", "Only model perfect people can have a lover" and so forth are superb reality creators as well as being very very depressing to ponder on at any length.

You can change these beliefs with EFT just as well as you can release bad feelings, because these are linked with feeling bad.

One of the worst types of emotions in relationships is being torn between love and hate, anger and forgiveness, fear and longing and any combination of feelings you can imagine.

You can use EFT to make peace between parts of you that are pulling you in opposite directions by using double statements with an "and" connection to express the conflict you are feeling, such as:

- "Being with her is destroying me AND I cannot live without her."
- "I want to leave him AND he is the father of our children who need him."
- "I love her AND I despise her."
- "I want him AND I hate myself for it."
- "I want to stand up to her AND there is nothing I can do."
- "I am terribly lonely AND I am terrified of being in a relationship."

If you find the "and" connection a little strained, you can say "but" instead; the main thing is that both the conflict partners are together in one sentence to release the feeling of see-sawing from one thing to the other or of feeling like you are tearing apart under the strain.

You can use more than two conflicting statements in one sentence if you need to when you do the tapping, as well.

Very useful in any relationship context is also Proxy Tapping.

It might be relevant to make the observation that people have relationships with many more things than just other people. Every form of relationship emotion from love to bitterness, bereavement and sadness, anger and so forth can be experienced towards all manner of things, from certain types of food to inanimate objects such as jewellery, stuffed toys and cars, animals and even landscapes, countries and houses.

These "relationship entanglements" are all successfully treatable with EFT and bring a great deal of relief, once they have been undone.

EFT & Sex

On the Meridian Therapy internet news group, a very experienced practitioner and EFT healer mailed for help with a client who hated sex following a childhood full of abuse. Now, this lady was married but could not bear to be touched. She loved her husband very much and lived in a constant hell of wanting to please him and have him be happy and satisfied, yet being unable to control her flinch-back and panic reflexes which would arise automatically and in spite of her husband having "been so patient for all these years".

Not much headway was being made with this lady although she seemed responsive to EFT in other ways; the therapist was wondering where she might be missing something, where she was going wrong.

As I looked over the kind of opening statements they had been using it became clear right away that both this lady and the therapist were backing away from "calling a spade a spade" - and this is the first lesson when we start using EFT for sex problems, fears, inadequacies, past trauma and bad experiences.

Whether we are working in self help by ourselves, or with other people, it matters not - oblique and roundabout descriptions of feelings, parts, acts and happenings don't work very well with EFT as we have noted elsewhere.

For many people, the whole topic of sex is so shocking, "dirty", unpleasant and generally contorted that there may be a lot of merit to just tap rounds of EFT on "those words" themselves and until they can be thought about and talked about without the energy system going into instant reversal and shame and embarrassment ensuing.

Sex is an area which might really have the very highest and least talked about emotions present, whether they may be in the forms of memories of trauma and abuse, or simply every day experiences of fear and failure.

If you remember the section on "EFT & Memories", you might also remember that things had to be described clearly, much as you might find in a court of law - what really happened then or what really happens now, step by step, and how you feel about it.

Gentling The Systems

A good place for anyone suffering from "shameful" problems of this nature is to tap the following soothing and strengthening statements, for example:

"Even though I don't want to think about this ..."
"Even though I just want to forget all about this ..."
"Even though I wish I would never have to think or talk about this ever again ..."
"Even though I feel sick at the thought of talking about this ..."
"Even though I am terrified at the thought of thinking about this again ..."

Please remember that EFT treatments are never meant to be something you force yourself or others to have to suffer through; we can start as way back when as we need to in order to make it as easy and gentle as possible to get real healing, change and forward movement into the systems of mind and body.

Starting From The Outside In

Especially sexual abuse survivors have symptoms that are clearly a direct result of what happened to them a long time ago but which are not necessarily directly related to having sex at all.

Many for example find it nearly impossible (or indeed, entirely impossible) to present themselves for intimate physical exams with a doctor or gynaecologist.

They may also experience problems about taking even top layers of clothes off in public (such as at the beach or in communal changing rooms) or other types of symptoms, from being unable to sleep with the window open even a little way or having to sit close to fire exits in restaurants - there are a multitude of symptoms.

Starting on these rather than on the memories, feelings or events directly is often a very good "way into" these frightening mindscapes.

I would make the comment that anyone who either knows or suspects that their sexual problems have been caused by abuse or trauma might consider seeking the aid of a qualified meridian energy therapist they feel really comfortable and safe with. Self help is a wonderful thing but indeed, some things are really better faced with a knowledgeable guide by ones side.

Should this apply to you, there is also the option of pre-treating fear or any reason to NOT go ahead and find resolution for these problems in self help first and use the EFT self treatments to get yourself to a place where you can ring up and make an appointment.

Treating Other Sexual Problems With EFT

This is of course a vast topic. This chapter is only designed to give you some ideas of what we can do with EFT, and that you can expect to see a real improvement in many areas of your sex life if you decide to use EFT in that centrally important context.

Performance & Relaxation

Whether it is male "performance" or female abilities to feel what the body can feel and flow with the sexual experience as we were designed to by God and the Universe, energy reversals and blockages are always something we can remove, treat and thus, get a great deal more out of our sex life.

We have already briefly touched on trauma and memories that can cause such reversals and energy blockages; here, I am particularly thinking about emotional responses which are indicators of other types of blockages such as:

Fear. Performance anxiety, thinking that you are not good enough, that there is something wrong with you, that you are "no good at sex" or that you don't deserve to have orgasms, that God thinks sex is bad or that you shouldn't be having it at all - these and a million more fears are the first and prime candidates to destroy the flow of energies through the systems and make our bodies cease up, cramp up in fear and panic and stop us from flowing with the sexual experience in an open and natural fashion.

All of these fears, if they are allowed to be expressed and treated with EFT, can and will recede and this really makes a **big** difference to your sexual experience.

Shame. Shame, guilt, disgust, distaste, embarrassment - these are really of one category and they are very difficult and painful emotions indeed that are guaranteed to keep an individual in sexual hell for their entire adult lives.

Interestingly, these forms of emotions which are very visceral with aspects of real physiological responses such as gagging responses, feelings of nausea and sickness, breathlessness etc, respond beautifully to the application of EFT and these are excellent self help candidates. In the privacy of your own home and your own mind and body, you can begin to treat such responses with the aid of your own body, or perhaps photographic or artistic representations of what is causing the problem.

I would make the side note that fetishes can be treated successfully with EFT, even if they have proven entirely untreatable with any other known method or approach; treating issues of shame and guilt **about** fetishes is also a very, very healing and reconciling thing to do and regardless whether an abatement in desire for the fetish is required or not.

Anger. Anger and feelings of rage at self or at others clearly preclude loving sexual flow in relationships – even with the self. Many people don't even know that they are angry at themselves or at their current partners; usually this is anger by proxy because it wasn't either the self or the current partner who ever did anything wrong to deserve this. Anger choked down causes big vortices and blockages in the energy system and causes sexual expression to become of a different flavour than it would otherwise have been. It also precludes honesty and intimacy in sexual relationships with self and others, so to treat anger and rage issues is always a good idea.

Here, I would like to clearly state that to have anger issues in any context, sexual or otherwise, isn't a character flaw or some genetic defect but simply and always a response to things that have happened to us in the past – it hurts and now I am angry in a very simple cause-and-effect.

EFT is particularly good at healing these old wounds and injuries once and for all, and when that happens, anger simply ceases to exist. It doesn't require a great deal of "forgiveness work" or any hardship other than to just simply repair the injuries in the energy system in the usual way, namely by firstly becoming aware of any issues of anger, giving them expression and doing the EFT treatment as usual with your own words, for example:

"Even though I still hate the man who raped me ..."
"Even though I despise and hate myself for not being more careful ..."
"Even though I hate my husband for constantly wanting sex ..."
"Even though all men are animals ..."
"Even though I hate myself for having sexual thoughts ..."
"Even though God hates me for having committed adultery ..."
"Even though I hate my body for wanting these disgusting things ..."

Every single anger, rage or hate you can release from yourself with EFT will be a burden released and help you think, feel and flow more freely.

Thoughts Of Shame and Morality

A great area of stopping people even trying to treat themselves so that they may release their energy blockages and reversals is in "thoughts of shame and morality" - things they were taught or things they believe.

For example, there are many people who think that if they liked sex any better than they did or didn't find it disgusting anymore, that would mean

162

that they would be out on the streets, doing it with everyone and everything, all the time.

This is absolutely not so and nothing but an old wives scare story.

Someone with sexual instincts which have returned to a state of natural flow will of course seek out sexual partners; but they will not be indiscriminate or stupid about it and much less develop into rapists or paedophiles. Quite in the contrary - those sorts of behaviours indicate a problem rather than ever representing any form of solution.

"Thoughts of shame and morality", as installed by fundamentalist religions for example, cause the most tremendous problems.

The drive to sexual expression is one of the most powerful forces we have in our adult lives and the fact is that if this expression (with a partner or by yourself) becomes mis-routed or perverted, of course we will have the corresponding powerful disturbances and "perversions", if you will.

Releasing blockages, untangling contortions and generally speaking, allowing the mind-body systems relating to being a sexual being to return to a state of health and flow cannot do anything else than to help make life easier, less stressful and more as it was always designed to be.

Magical Sexual Energy Flow

Discussing truthful opening statements and working together with EFT in a partnership to help both partners achieve deeper, more profound and more exhilarating experiences is a truly magical thing.

There are many variations on "Partner EFT" – just sitting opposite one another and touching the points on each other, mirror fashion, either in silence or whilst both say an affirmation or statement of love or intent to change something for one or both of the partners is absolutely fascinating and more intense than most practised tantra specialists achieve as a rule.

163

Allowing each other to help each other remove the last blockages and reservations, fears or contortions to experiencing true intimacy with each other is one of the most extraordinary things you could possibly do in a relationship, no matter how you achieve this; gentle touching rather than tapping can keep this process loving and entirely flowing and non-mechanical.

Including the EFT points in a massage can be used easily and without having to say too much; kissing them is a more advanced version which I particularly enjoy, especially when it comes with an opening statement of, "I love you and I desire you."

If you do not have a partner, doing EFT for your own hopes and dreams, fears and limitations in an intimate setting with yourself is a breakthrough experience of learning to love yourself in every way if you will allow yourself to have it.

Celibacy & Spiritual Energy Flow

There are many people who for one reason or the other wish to use sexual energy not for sexual expression in partnership but for other purposes, such as raising energy for healing or spiritual development.

I would point out that we still are in a place where the sexual energies themselves must flow freely first **before** they can be transmuted into something else. If these energies are blocked or disturbed, they cannot function in the spiritual flow either – no matter what, and no matter how, sexual energies need to flow freely, lightly and cleanly, without contortions and blockages.

I think that having one's sexual systems in order might well account for at least 30% of any one adult's effectivity and happiness in this life. This doesn't mean they have to have sex at all; and it doesn't mean they have to have a partner. What we do need however is to address our injuries and disturbances in these systems urgently and as one of the first and most important areas of enquiry when there is something wrong with our lives. EFT gives us a tool at last with which to do this, without fear, shame or guilt.

EFT & Speaking Out

It is truly remarkable how many problems that people have in their lives come down in the end to the topic of "speaking out" or "speaking up for yourself".

Of course, I was very familiar with this in the context of public speaking where this special type of fear is really brought to our attention with force; I was also familiar with it in the context of artistic stage performances and "stage fright".

It was not until I began to train people in the old art of "Story Telling" that it came to my attention how much else is linked into being unable to "say what's on your mind."

This extends to:

Being able to speak up inside relationships – this is one of the deep core, very structural problems central to relationships that people really cannot say what's really troubling them, what they really want and need from each other, because they're simply too afraid of what would happen if they did.

- **Being able to stand up for yourself** – an absolutely essential "skill" in every day interactions, be it at work, when employing others, to simply shopping in a supermarket or making sure you get the service you deserve in an expensive restaurant. The popularity and true need for "assertiveness training" comes as a result of not being able to speak up for oneself and needing aggression or withdrawal to come to the rescue for every day survival.

- **Being able to express yourself creatively** – or perhaps I should say, being able to express yourself at all, creatively or otherwise. I am simply appalled how many people, intelligent, very, very knowledgeable, experienced, wise and filled with rich knowings and learning can't even post a mail to a public newsgroup, never mind write a cohesive article or even attempt to express themselves in art, music,

165

poetry or any other of the many media we have at our disposal.

- **To be able to express who you are** – this is a deep and basic fear of rejection which is part and parcel of not this whole "not speaking up for yourself" deal and it goes into what clothes one would choose, what kind of hair colour one might need to have, what body, what profession, how much money one would need and so forth.

When this failure to "speak up for yourself" backs up deeply enough and for a long period of time, a person may not even be able to **tell themselves** or even **know** in consciousness what they want, what they need, what they desire, because this "not speaking up" has become so habitual, it even extends into your own thoughts.

I really haven't met anyone yet who would not derive some benefits from considering a question such as,

"What would happen if I really told the truth (in my work, in this relationship, about myself, etc)?"

... because this does unearth deep, basic fears which distort our energy systems and do wide ranging harm over a wide ranging number of topics, probably impacting just about everything in our lives.

EFT & Spirituality

It is a fact that there's nothing to break the natural connection we feel with the universe in general and God in particular as effectively as negative emotions do.

Even if users of EFT don't look for any improvement in that area, it often happens quite naturally as a result of releasing all kinds of fears, tensions and stresses that "all of a sudden, my eyes were opened to the beauty of creation", as one lady so wonderfully put it.

People to whom spirituality is a major concern have in EFT a wonderful tool to overcome problems and resolve conflicts of all kinds.

One gentleman, a holistic counsellor, very much wanted "to do God's work". But he felt uncomfortable and apologetic even as he said the words, and was shaking his head "No!" at the same time as speaking them. After tapping for, "I want to do God's work", it occurred to him that there was a part of him that believed he was entirely unworthy, having done some things in his life that were not always totally perfect in every way.

He then tapped for being unworthy to do God's work. What happened after that was most moving and deeply resonant and releasing - I remember this particular session with a deep sense of awe. The gentleman in question has reached a whole new level of satisfaction in his work since and reports a deep sense of peace and healing pervading him now.

A lady I recall tapped for, "I don't believe in miracles". She felt that if only she could really believe that, they would be given a chance to manifest for her; yet another lady tapped for, "Even though I don't know what I have to do to get closer to Jesus". It turned out that there was nothing she had to do but to accept that she was loved already just the way she was. The moment when she realised this marked a transformation of her life in more ways than I can describe to you.

The last example that springs to mind here was a lady who was struggling with a number of very serious gender related issues and at one point, angrily remarked, "Of course, not even God likes women." She had been brought up in a faith where women were deemed unclean and where not allowed to hold any ministerial duties, nor even touch religious artefacts or stand too close to relics and altars.

Tapping for this statement healed her in many ways, and went a long way to resolve many of her other gender issues.

EFT & Sports

What is the difference between a winning horse and an also ran? Usually, as little as half a length after a mile long race.

I have used EFT with a variety of sports people and I can only say, whatever sport you do, this will make so much difference, you won't believe it. Let's take the US No1 sport, golf, as an example. This is so popular now as an EFT application, there exists an entire dedicated golfers network where practitioners and EFT-using golfers share their successes and their experiences, because golfers are extremely aware of how your states of mind control the outcome of a competition - they even call golf "the mental game".

Here are a couple of examples. Even if you can't stand golf, read them with a view to the underlying principles that apply absolutely anywhere a human being steps up to the challenge of performing the best they can on command at a given moment.

Steve, an accountant, was a good golfer but as he said, "Hopeless with woods". Three rounds of tapping later which uncovered that his first instructor had held forth at great length how difficult woods are to control, how they are longer, heavier and less accurate. Once this was resolved, he whacked one ball after the other, straight as a die, down the practise run in high gusting winds. It took nearly 20 balls before he had managed to convince himself that the problem was well and truly overcome!

Peter, a golf pro and a very, very talented player, had the following problem:

If he was in a competition and all went well, he would usually win. But if he made even the tiniest mistake, he would immediately start to berate himself internally brutally and viciously and his game would fall to pieces. Not surprisingly, lately this had become worse and worse and he was more tense and more likely to make mistakes, with every competition he entered.

He actually had to start the tapping with, "Even though I don't accept myself at all, I fully and profoundly accept myself" - his problem was rooted in trying to attain perfection in everything he did. Once this was resolved successfully, not only did his game and his results improve dramatically, but he also began to enjoy competing far more than he had ever done.

And now for something completely different, which illustrates another reason for problems whilst competing:

Jenny is a competitive gun dog trainer. This is a very complex sport which relies not only on the dog being trained exceptionally well as a wide variety of skills are required, from swimming to scenting to quartering to retrieving to remaining focussed on the job in hand, but also on the handler keeping their emotions together on the day and presenting a similar frame of mind to the dog as was present during their practise time together.

As is the case for any sport, in her back yard the dogs were absolutely brilliant but everything would fall apart as soon as the event arrived.

Jenny tapped for a great variety of issues, from being nervous of the judges, being worried what spectators might think, not trusting the dogs or her training of the dogs and all of this helped tremendously. Still, she didn't win much although she enjoyed her outings far more. Then one day, she realised that the cause of this was a deep-seated belief she had held since childhood, "I will never be amongst the winners". Following her tapping for this statement, her dogs virtually swept the board at the following event and have been doing so ever since.

Whatever the sport, EFT opens the door for every day people to attain a clarity of thought and a focus of purpose that was previously only available to top athletes and only through many years of constant mental practise and rigid discipline.

EFT & Telephones

Once you know how to do EFT, you can teach others how to do this over the telephone. Many people have said how helpful this has been, from professional therapists who can help bedridden, imprisoned and housebound folk, to people being able to help friends and relatives on the other side of the country, or even in some cases, on the other side of the world.

Like any session, the first thing is for the telephone client to learn the points and how to tap them. Some therapists send out material before the actual session such as a large chart with the points clearly marked, to cut down on explanations and time and for the client to refer to as the process unfolds. But it's perfectly possible to just explain where the points are, it just takes a little longer.

It can be helpful to tap on the microphone part of the telephone and have the listener do the same to judge how fast to tap, and with how much strength. Some people "hit" themselves too hard, and others don't put enough energy into the process, so this is a good way to adjust the strength of their tapping when you can't see them.

The second part, where the problem is discussed and the therapist listens carefully for tell tale statements that will later be used for starting affirmations and to tap on, is not so different from a face-to-face session. For someone who hasn't done so consciously before, it is amazing how much you can tell through someone's breathing patterns and changes in their tone of voice about their state of mind.

Any EFTer who does telephone consultations on a regular basis will know how much it sharpens one's perception of these things, and how, in some cases, these indicators are far more immediate and accurate than visually noticeable changes can be.

The third part is to start the process and to guide the other person through it. As always, deep sighs, the onset or cessation of weeping, yawns, changes in the person's voice or way of speaking, all tell when an energy shift is taking place. This can take a while, and it is important not to hurry through this. Some long standing problems do have many aspects.

The last step is to test for the change. This is either done using something like the VOC scale or SUDS levels - the person is asked to rate their own internal changes; but with the advent of mobile phones, real tests for things such as spider phobias can be done by the client walking into a pet shop with the therapist a thousand miles away on stand by - just in case there was an aspect that was overlooked!

EFT & Testing

Testing, i.e. finding some way to try out in practise how well the problem has been resolved, is absolutely essential, whether you are working on your own, or with a therapist or a friend.

Not only does a good test tell the you when the work has been successfully completed, it also ratifies the change to the conscious mind - the energy therapies can work so rapidly that a problem can be completely healed yet the person has had the problem for so long, they simply cannot believe it has really gone away.

I've had a number of clients who did some work on a particular issue and said they felt much happier about it.

Upon checking back with them a couple of weeks later, they still hadn't attempted to do the thing that had caused them the problems, because they felt good and happy and didn't want to disappoint themselves in case it came back!

In every case, I managed to encourage the person to attempt the frightening thing, instructing them to stop should there be any indications of the fear returning at all. Out of five people, only one reported there was fear remaining, the other four all found to their utter astonishment that the problem had really disappeared and they were not only doing things easily that had been absolutely impossible to them before, they were even enjoying themselves.

It is important to know that if the test "fails" that doesn't mean EFT hasn't worked, it just means there's some more work to be done to release the problem fully and completely, once and for all.

One client used EFT by himself at home to overcome a great fear of going into art shops and getting the proprietors to buy or exhibit his paintings. He had dealt with many issues to do with rejection, having to face an authority figure, selling himself, fear of success etc. etc. etc., but he was still afraid to go to the shops and was beginning to think that EFT hadn't worked in this instance, although it had helped him profoundly with other issues. (A note: If EFT works for you, it works. Full Stop. It will work on any and every issue with a bit of perseverance and sometimes, a bit of extra insight from another. If it works on one thing but not another, you haven't found the right leverage point yet or there are objections to not having the problem anymore that haven't been answered yet).

I asked him to go through the process of entering the shop and conducting the talk with the manager/proprietor, in his mind, step by step. It turned out that there was one fear he hadn't thought of to tap for, namely the time when he would stand in the shop and the owner would be busy with paying clients. He was concerned that he would have to wait "and kind of mill around aimlessly, getting more and more nervous".

Once this surprising and unexpected aspect had been tapped free of any feelings of embarrassment and fear, he virtually rushed down to the shops after the session - the final block on the road to achieving success had been cleared.

If you are working with a therapist, they should endeavour to test how well the intervention worked as best as possible under the circumstances - this is usually done by having the client imagining the situation that caused the problems and the therapist encouraging the client as best they can to find out if they can still have the emotions.

This technique is called the "MindWalk" and although it is not as convincing as a real life test, but usually very accurate. See also Persuasion, Fear of Flying.

If you are working by yourself, do remember to test yourself. It is a most important part of the treatment process and it is essential for you to be able to be really sure on all levels that the problem has, indeed, disappeared.

EFT & Therapists

If you see many very unhappy, ill or even disturbed people day in, day out, for a period of many years, it is well known that some of this negativity may rub off on you eventually.

There are a number of ways EFT can be used to help with therapist's combat fatigue; but even if you are not a therapist, I would strongly encourage you to look closely at this section.

Undoubtedly, you have some acquaintances, friends, colleagues or family members who leave you feeling drained, exhausted and exasperated after a "session" with them!

1. Low Energy

If you feel drained after a session, doing a round or two of EFT can restore your energy levels and your spirits. Use general set up phrases such as "I am whole and healthy in mind and body and I deeply and profoundly accept and love myself". It might also be interesting to find out just why this happens with certain people and what you can do to stop it from happening in the first place - investigative tapping or question tapping such as "Even though I don't know how I can protect myself from vampires ..." may get you on track towards the right answer.

2. Resonant Problems (Projection)

Sometimes, the client will bring an issue that resonates with you. You might have experienced the same problem in the past, or just by talking with or taking care of the client, you become aware that you have a similar problem which has not yet been resolved. It can also happen that you notice a particularly strong "gut reaction" to a client's problems, which is always an indication that you have an issue of some kind which wishes to be addressed. A quick tap after the client has left on what was revealed to you through this mechanism can be most helpful and supportive. Using EFT in this way could truly lead to healers healing themselves - each client becomes a potential mirror to help find out what your own problems still are.

3. Strong Personal Feelings (Transference)

It is generally held that strong personal feelings, either of like or dislike, tend to get in the way when you're trying to do any kind of healing or therapy. Wholehearted, unconditional love for the client on the other hand does not come into that category because it isn't a feeling but a state of being which springs from a wonderfully calm and centred state of mind. EFT is truly a most helpful tool in being able to move into this mental state with far more ease in future.

If you hated the client, found them or their problems repulsive, or alternatively, irresistibly attractive and wanted them to move in with you on the spot, take the time to deal with the underlying issues after the session. This is not only healing, it is most revealing and can become one of the greatest gifts that particular client will ever receive from any therapist.

4. Outcome Attachment

This heading means that the therapist (or friend, or mother!) gets disheartened, disappointed or angry if the client doesn't make the gains from the treatment or advise that they should. There are many reasons why some folk simply don't seem to get any better (and Psychological Reversal for some core issues should always be looked at in those cases), but the fact is that therapists are therapists because they want to help people, heal people, and it drives many of them crazy if they're doing all they can and the client is simply not responding in the way they desire.

Much lip service is given in the field to the idea that each person heals at their own rate, have their own path, are in charge of their own destiny - but at the end of the day, many therapists are thoroughly unhappy when they don't get "the results". EFT can take the continuous performance pressure to heal like Jesus off anyone's shoulders who is afflicted with this particular problem and help reconnect the therapist with their patience and the deep faith that, indeed, "the universe is unfolding as it must".

Taking the time to sit down after a client has left and to engage in just five minutes of "basic therapist's maintenance" as I call it, can make a lot of difference to your work and your levels of energy and enjoyment.

EFT & Trophy Memories

The rather unfortunate term "trophy memories" denotes memories that have been examined and communicated in consciousness many times before; this may have been in traditional counselling or psychotherapy, or simply as stories told repeatedly to friends and relatives.

These trophy memories itself have a deep emotional charge behind them; in order to communicate them reasonably safely, the human mind creates what I call a veil over them which allows a person to speak of them quite calmly and without needing to access the emotional charge directly which would be far too painful.

What happens over time is that the person in question doesn't feel much or even anything at all when they refer to these kinds of events and they may conclude that the event has been entirely resolved and they have "gotten over it", "have forgiven everything" or that "time has healed it".

It has been my experience that even 40 years of psychoanalysis and continued talking about and re-examining certain events can have done little or nothing to heal such underlying traumas. Fellow counsellors, too, report that all kinds of issues that people thought were resolved long ago turn out to be nothing of the sort once one starts to apply EFT.

Here's what one lady said,

"I was working with my son on a fear of driving using EFT. He traced the start of this back to a time when I had left him with my ex-husband. As soon as he said these words, it was as though I was catapulted through time, straight back to that most terrible time in my life, when I had walked away from my children. The pain was so intense, I couldn't breathe and was in shock. I couldn't believe it, I had had so much counselling, I had cried buckets, I had done so much work with so many

176

different therapies, I truly believed that I had resolved this a long time ago. But yet here it was, as raw and as painful as ever - no wonder I had not made the gains in my life that I had hoped to make! What followed was the most intensive EFT session I have ever experienced, and at the end of it, I was exhausted and yet triumphant in a strange way. I can honestly say now, I have finally forgiven myself."

I have many personal and testimonial examples of a similar nature - namely that what we thought was healed had just been buried more profoundly. EFT can truly heal these issues; for this reason I would suggest that if you have one or more of such memories as described above, please revisit them carefully one more time to make sure they're really healed and not just veiled.

EFT & Weight Loss

It must be said that before we even start with this chapter, I dislike the term weight loss and the only reason it is allowed to be a chapter heading in one of my books is so people can find it who are probably looking for a variation of having a fit and healthy body that is in proportion to their size and type.

As such, "weight loss" is then nothing but a subdivision of health, and that would be overall health as in "a healthy mind in a healthy body".
The mind aspect is particularly important because a great many people are trying to achieve via thinning themselves down (to preferably nothing more than a skeleton!) something that cannot be achieved in that way – namely love, respect and happiness.

A young lady of 26 years said, "I was trying to make as an actress. But my coach kept saying, you're too fat, you need to loose 50 pounds, then we'll see. So I did. I became bulimic. I lost the fifty pounds and then another 30, and that was the best time of my life I've ever known. The coach loved me and treated me in preference. I got called back for auditions. I got invited to parties. I was loved."

She said this in a low whisper, lying like a desiccated corpse in a hospital bed, the sheet outlining a pitiful body made only from bones with tubes everywhere. She had little hair left and her teeth were falling out. She was perhaps a week or two away from death. And the truth was that those people who invited her to parties and gave her attention and preferential treatment **did not love her**. They were using her for their own reasons instead - the trade was always flawed.

The first and foremost consideration with weightloss, and it really doesn't matter if we are only talking about a few pounds here and there so last year's swim suit fits again or having to turn around years of habits and behaviours which have resulted in a grossly overweight body, must be a will towards health rather than anything else because that is the only safe foundation in the long run that motivates correctly and that can never be broken, no matter what disappointments, outward circumstances or what people say or do.

- A healthy weight (a healthy body) only comes from within and it's true, we all know that already.

- A healthy body glows and becomes very attractive to people with whom one might want to develop a relationship (as opposed to people who wish to exploit a person for their own purposes, such as TV directors, fashion agents and pimps).

- A healthy body helps to attract all those things which people who have weight conflicts always wanted in the first place – attention, positive regard, admiration and finally, love.

To switch the focus from what is wrong with our bodies to what we want to achieve, what we deserve and what our body and mind needs from us so it can serve us in the best way possible, in the process getting for us all we ever wanted from the world, from our lives, from other people and from ourselves as well, is a true step in the right direction not towards just "weight loss" but personal growth, joy and true happiness.

Do you want to be healthy?

This is surely the first question we must ask, and very often, the answer to is "Oh sure," at first but then, when we dig a bit more deeply, we tend to find objections and rejections of many different kinds.
The idea of "well first I lose some weight, then I'll be healthy" is also one of these proverbial carts before the horse – it is the wrong way around in any way you might imagine.

You have got to be moving towards health first – and then the body will begin to re-balance, the mind will begin to calm, and the metabolism will be changing which will reflect in a different body shape as the result.

So now, please sit down and make a note of what your feelings are on the idea of wanting to be healthy, and most importantly, what objections you might have to this – including the idea that it would take far too long and the party with the big producer is just 2 weeks away, so just stopping to eat altogether is what is necessary right now and the health can wait ...

When we address real questions of health and especially, long term health and "glowing from within" as the actual goal of a treatment that started out as a "weight loss treatment", we get into real self discovery country and the reasons for why we might have ever considered to choose differently become revealed.

This is truly change and human development then and not just losing a few pounds for the summer season.

I debated with myself whether I should mention this at all but in truth, I was hoping some would read this and really change their minds about why they are seeking weightloss, and step off that strange addiction ladder to weightloss and exercise and instead, consider some alternatives to really getting what they always wanted out of life – for their body to be happy, for their minds and spirits to be happy and soaring, and for all of it to work together in harmony and love.

But now, on to the more common forms of using EFT for weightloss purposes.

Reducing Cravings, Eating Less

Of course, many of us are addicted to eating rather unhealthy foods, especially if they are eaten compulsively or all the time.

Ice cream, hamburgers, snacks, cakes and chocolates are inextricably linked with party time, with treats, with joyful holidays and with celebrations and apart from any physiological reasons for liking them or wanting them, never mind craving them or using them to get a sense of happiness into our otherwise miserable lives, that's the main hook.

This can quite easily be undone using EFT by simply having an example of the food item to hand, looking at it, smelling it and tapping either in silence or with an opening statement such as, "Even though I really crave (hunger for) this (item), I deeply and profoundly love and accept myself."

Tens of thousands of people attest to the fact that once the "celebration contortion" has been removed from the simple food item, it becomes nothing more and nothing less than just a rather unattractive thing that isn't very good for you and that you really don't want anymore.

Try it for yourself – it is an interesting sensation when the cravings are "tapped away".

You can of course use this approach anywhere and not just at the "eating point" – you can have a little tap in supermarkets at the purchase point, in restaurants at the choice point and in all and every situation where a craving might strike.

"Eating" As A Replacement

Eating is not only about food and taste, we all know that. People use eating – the very first thing beyond breathing we do for survival from the moment we are born! – for all kinds of replacement activities.

The oft cited "boredom" for example, that causes people who live alone to go on expeditions to the fridge repeatedly in an evening of TV viewing, could be anything from loneliness to wanting sex instead, if only we knew it.

We can use EFT to just tap for boredom to help overcome this, for example:

"Even though I am bored, I deeply and profoundly love and accept myself."

... and simply find out what turns up. Sometimes, this will alleviate the "hunger" all by itself and you just get on with life. At other times, you might get an idea of what you would like to do instead and sometimes, you might even get an insight on what it is you really wanted – company, sex, an exciting surprise or perhaps an outing, a walk, a bath or a million other possible things.

People will also use eating to stop themselves from doing something else, much as they use work, substance addictions and all sorts of other replacement activities.

Sometimes it is enough to just tap it away, other times it becomes apparent that deeper work or more tapping on other topics is what is required here.

Something that many people have found very useful is to tap on, "Even though I don't know what I really hunger for, I deeply and profoundly love and accept myself."

Using EFT For Hunger Pains

It is often said about people who are veterans of the weight war that they no longer have any idea at all when their body is either requesting food or asking for food deliveries to stop because their feedback systems have become so perverted and scrambled.

For anyone wishing to get off the weight gain – weight loss addiction roundabout, it is a good idea to try and unscramble these feedback systems and when either hunger pains turn up or the converse, namely that you should be hungry by now but you are not, to treat this with EFT. Opening statements might be, "I really can't tell anymore when I'm really hungry and when I'm just craving and I deeply and profoundly love and accept myself." – "I can't hear my body's signals to tell me to stop." – "I don't trust my body anymore." – "My body doesn't trust me anymore." and other truthful treatments of what it is really like to be you, in your body.

I am writing this because I know that people abuse health systems of any kind in order to "switch off all hunger sensations" so they may starve themselves even more successfully. I would truly hate for anyone to try and use EFT in this fashion and if you feel that you would like to do this thing, I'd ask you to stop and think.

You don't want to become a starving skeleton more than the next anorexic on the drip in the hospital bed and the truth is, you want to be just the best you can be – the healthiest, the strongest, the most glowing and most loveable entity you can possibly be. That is the truth of any person, no matter how and when things may have come unstuck or off track and EFT can really help you with that, building health and good relations with your body from the ground up.

By all means, use it to really cure false cravings and untangle false attachments; allow what seems like hunger but actually is a help call for something else to be soothed and alleviated. That is what EFT is for and that's what will get you what you want if you use it in the right way – quickly, at that, so there are no excuses for EFT abuse.

Using EFT For Goals Of Weight, Health & Beauty

You might have heard the idea to tape a picture of a thin person to the fridge by the way of giving the unconscious mind something to work towards.

This might or might not work, but doing EFT sessions to establish and more importantly, understand and make sure that you have indeed the right goals for your various health and beauty endeavours is a very, very useful thing indeed.

Bringing out a picture of yourself at a younger and/or slimmer stage of life and tapping on the ideas and thoughts this produces can be extremely helpful to make sure that you are not accidentally trying to "regain your lost youth" rather than having your now-glowing-health instead – you can imagine that the first can lead to nothing but misery in the long run and the latter is clearly much more healthy in every way.
Photographs or magazine pictures of "goal models" and tapping on the ideas this produces is also extremely useful for anyone engaged in any weightloss activities.

Once again, here we get to know what we are really thinking and feeling, what our real beliefs are and if they need working on. Feelings of inadequacy, ugliness, shame, failure and the like comparing oneself to model images produces causes nothing but chaos inside our bodies and minds and that doesn't help either with weightloss or with the far more important "glowing health" as you can imagine.

Thoughts About Fat, Being Fat & Fat People

For true, long term glowing health and not just yoyo weight gain-weight loss addiction games, there is some merit in facing one's own thoughts about being fat and what that means.

From decisions such as, "I have no will power and I am weak", to "it means I'm ugly and unlovable", "it means I'm worthless, dirty and disgusting", I'm sure you'll have your own ideas of what it means to be a fat person in today's societies.

I would make the comment that of course, the older ones amongst us were brought up by very, very different people than we have today, namely by people who remember the truth of starvation and hunger and who would judge their success as a parent or provider by the glossy fatness of their dependents. These older VS younger societal beliefs set up tremendous conflicts because once upon a time it was true that fat was equal to rich and thin equal to poor; whereas nowadays it is exactly the opposite. If someone is in possession of both sets of beliefs, both will need to be addressed and basically, tapped away so the person may be free to choose glowing health instead and as an absolute conviction of truth and practicality in all ways.

Happy And Healthy

Happy and healthy go hand in hand. Someone who is truly happy and dances through life with excitement and expectation of good things happening to them will find health is a side effect that isn't hard and wasn't even something they consciously had to work at.

An example is that of a fat person who finds a new love and immediately, they begin to lose weight – it isn't difficult at all, it just happens.

So let's be sensible in the context of "weight loss" and consider that **anything we do to make ourselves happier** will of course be the best diet aid you could ever prescribe yourself, and definitely the most powerful.

So, in EFT self treatments for health, ask yourself what YOU need to be more happy, to have a happier life, to feel happier more often and use EFT to treat whatever it is that stands in your way. Even external circumstances such as "being stuck at home with two screaming children" need not actually preclude happiness or the experience of happiness at all if you can approach it in the right way – so a round or two on, "Even though the kids are driving me crazy/ruining my life/destroying my happiness/etc/etc" can release stress, relax a situation and – yes, that's right, make your life happier.

You don't have to go to instant and everlasting bliss right away, just as you don't have to go from 250lbs to 30lbs – it is not like that. The more little bits of happiness there are in your life, the more the overall happiness mounts up, just as much as the little tiny bits of food morsels here and there, all the time, mount up to mountains of fat over time!

I believe absolutely that the real, true antidote to fat is happiness.

So I will end this section on ideas how you can start EFT to help you towards true health and well being with the suggestion and all my encouragement to use EFT in every area of your life you can think of to make things easier, flow more smoothly and make room for health and for happiness.

EFT & Willpower

For almost everyone in every society, having "a lot of willpower" to run roughshod over one's personal inclinations, emotions, bodies, intuitions, fears and uncertainties is some kind of perverse badge of honour.

For EFTers on the other hand, willpower is a diagnostic tool to tell you when you're still not done with a particular presenting issue; if you still have to use it, no matter how slightly, the problem has not yet been entirely resolved.

I had never come across this view on willpower before, but when I did, it opened my eyes to a scary reality - namely, that people seem to have constructed a world and a way of living within it which forces the misuse of willpower from the second you wake up in the morning, to the second you drop your head on your pillow at night.

The alarm clock beeps - you don't want to get up. So you force your weary body out of bed. That's just normal, right? WRONG and wrong in capital letters! Let's back up and have a look at this.

Why does a person have to use willpower to start their day?

Could it be that the day doesn't hold a rich and wondrous tapestry of unfolding pleasant and even ecstatic events which the person in question simply cannot wait to partake of?

Could it be that their body told them the night before many times how tired it was and how much it wanted to stop (drinking/typing/reading/ watching TV/etc. etc. etc.) and it had been overridden, yet again, by the application of willpower?

Could it be that the person didn't sleep very well and tossed and turned at night, worried, frightened of the future, burdened with so many unresolved wants, needs, desires and conflicts that they followed them right into their dreams?

Whichever way you look at it and whatever the reason for any particular person to feel like I've described when they wake up in the mornings, there's always issues presenting themselves that, if they had been resolved in some way (and in our case here, through the application of EFT with these issues) the person in question would no longer need to "force their weary body" out of bed.

The realisation of how much we misuse willpower every day in every way, was close to an enlightenment experience to me; I would urge you too, to make a mental note of how and when you are applying willpower to force yourself to do things against yourself, and to begin to wonder how these internal conflicts might be resolved, healed and released.

But let's go back to willpower as a diagnostic tool for a moment. One example that springs to mind was an agoraphobic lady who had not left her house in the last five years. On approach towards the door, her steps began to falter - a classic indication that she was forcing herself to take those steps and that there was already fear present that was trying to stop her. We backed up to a "safe place" where there was no fear, and began tapping. After each round, she found she could move forward a little further, and even remarked, "I could make myself go to the door now."

In most every form of therapy, this statement would have been grounds for celebration, but not so with EFT. We are not looking to diminish a fear enough so the person can "make themselves" do anything at all, we are looking to completely eliminate the internal resistance so the person "WANTS" to do the thing that had caused the problems in the past.

A few more rounds of tapping, and what I call "the flip" had occurred. With the fear completely gone, the lady in question now couldn't wait to leave the house, and became impatient with me when I tried to hold her back. She virtually ran out of the house and into the front garden and then stood there, laughing and laughing until there were tears streaming from her eyes - because being outside felt GOOD to her.

This is a great concluding section to this section, because it illustrates a point that has come up previously a number of times so well: When you treat yourself with EFT, previously scary things become fun to do. That is what you're looking for, that is the achievement you're after in every single case.

It's not enough to "not be afraid anymore". There is a realm beyond, in which you take delight in the activity/your body/your health/your work and your life.

That is the promise and the prospect of working with EFT.

Accept nothing less.

PART IV - FLEXIBLE APPROACHES

As we've said before, EFT is a **content free structure** you can apply any time, and any where there is a problem that has an emotional content.

This basic structure is extremely flexible and can be changed in many different ways to suit an individual persons preferences. In fact, it is pretty impossible to do EFT for any length of time by yourself or with clients and not modify the basic recipe in some way. If you are going to study the field of meridian therapies further, you will come across many "cousins" of EFT and you will note that many are based on just a small modification of the original system.

Here is a round up of some of the approaches that are common to accommodate client preferences or personal preferences. You might try some of these for yourself and probably, go on to invent your own ones along the way.

1. To Tap or Not To Tap ...?

There are many different ways to stimulate the points that are used in the EFT protocol besides tapping them. We have already mentioned some of them in the previous chapters, but here there are again in list form for your convenience:

a) Touch & Breathe (TAB)

Originally developed by John Diepold, this is EFT but you don't tap the points, you just touch them (hold them) and breathe in and out once whilst focussing on the problem.

This can be very calming for stressed out or overanxious people, and some children much prefer it to being tapped. It further has the advantage that it can be done surreptitiously whilst sitting on a bus or any other public situation, for that matter. It's also very useful as an alternative when there is physical pain on or near the tapping points (such as in cases of toothaches, migraines, and general injuries).

b) Massaging The Points

Instead of tapping or tabbing, you can rub the points or make a circular massaging movement with one finger. This is used in Tellington T Touch and said to be very effective.

c) Intention Tapping

Some people find it very easy to just focus their minds on the points and accomplish the tapping sequence in that way. Some imagine themselves tapping, some imagine beams of light entering the points, some talk of "stroking the points with their minds". Try it out and if you can make it work, this is a great help for when you're in bed, can't be seen to tap or cannot physically tap for whatever reason.

d) Chords

This is the term coined for holding more than one point at the same time. Some people find interesting benefits in doing both collarbone points at the same time, for example, or holding the point under the eye and then the gamut point with the spare hand. As there are so many permutations on this particular theme, you can well imagine that there's a lot of it about and much written about this.

Play with it and remember to reality-check everything by testing your results thoroughly.

Getting the shifts is what counts in the end.

2. Tapping Less, Tapping Some More …

There are thousands more points on the body that have impact on the flowing of the meridians. The EFT points you have learned were chosen because they are so globally applicable and work so well for the vast majority of people.

Sometimes, and for whatever reason, points can be left out of the procedure and the protocol still work just fine; it is not absolutely necessary to tap all of the points each time.

For example, when you are tapping on another person, it is sometimes wise to leave out the Under Arm spot because this is a more "private" area than the rest of the points.

Some people find after a while that they don't need the 9 Gamut procedure to create a shift, others find that they don't need to do the finger points to feel better instantly. There's a lot of personal preference in these things, and as you read this, remember to go back to the Basic Recipe in case your short cut techniques have not brought the desired results.

On the other hand, some people have added points they find useful and include them in their own personal recipe.

Some of the favourites are:

- Top Of The Head (Crown)
- Third Eye
- Thymus (a round raised area in the centre of your chest just beneath the collar bone)
- Under Breast (both sides, in line with the nipples, about three ribs up; or the end points of this meridian which are in line with the nipples just where your ribcage ends.

As you learn more about meridian therapies, you will come across many more such points, all of which are thought to be important meridian junctions.

Some people then go off and create terribly complicated treatment routines, which is really not in the spirit of EFT – the beauty of EFT is its simplicity and that it works so well with over 85% of the population.

I would therefore advise to do the basic EFT first, and only in the few and very far between cases where you're not getting a response, to bring in some of the extra points to see if it makes a difference.

3. Fail Safes

If you are working with others, it happens on occasion that the SUDs levels don't drop as fast as you would expect them to. Now before we go into Fail Safes, I would most strongly recommend to look at these following reasons for this BEFORE simply assuming that the basic EFT process "didn't work" in this particular instance:

- You've Got The Wrong Opening Statement.

This is incredibly common and usually simply a misunderstanding. Sometimes you can think you know what the problem is but you were simply wrong. Tapping a set for, "Even though I don't know why this isn't going down" can help.

- There Is A Major Unanswered Objection.

A person will hold on to a problem with everything they've got if they think (even unconsciously) that there is a good reason for having the problem, and that getting rid of the problem will make their life even worse in some way. Keeping the problem will have a major and very important benefit, or, the person might think they lack the resources to continue without whatever it was that the problem provided.

This is known as Primary Gain and can even be the very reason why someone had created a problem in the first place.

Finding these reasons and tapping for them first is perhaps the second most common approach and it will open the way for a simple round of EFT to clear the problem eventually.

Suggested start ups for this "clearing the way" could be:

- "Even though I don't think I can cope without (insert benefit of problem)",
- "Even though I don't know how I will live my life without (insert problem)",

193

- "Even though I will lose my identity if I lose this problem",
- "Even though I don't deserve to get over this problem".

… or whatever objections reveal themselves. Please be sure to have read the "Primary Gain" section in the A-Z with care.

- There Is An Undiscovered Order And Sequence To Solving This Problem

Sometimes a problem cannot be solved by itself and before something else needs to be done first.

It can be useful to simply ask if a problem won't move, "What do I need to (have, be, do, experience, understand, know, forget about, change my mind about) FIRST and before this problem can resolve?"

- The Person Can't Contact Emotions In The First Place

This is not very common, but some people really cannot get in touch with their emotions easily, or perhaps even not at all.

What happens then is that they don't really feel anything to start with, but they KNOW that it's a big problem so they give it a high SUDs rating. After the round, they don't feel any different and say quite truthfully that they don't feel any better and nothing has changed.

This type of person can be made to go through all kinds of different fail safes and the answer will always remain the same, "Nope, still don't feel anything."

Interestingly enough, that is not an indicator that their problem has not, in fact, been partially or even completely released.

If you come across such a person, first set up a treatment that can be tested easily, i.e. something where their behaviour will give you feedback on whether the treatment has worked rather than them telling you about it. Ask them about something they cannot do, or find very difficult to do, have them focus on it, do EFT and then test. Very often, the test will be positive – the change has taken place.

Working without feedback through emotion, physiological signs, words and descriptions of internal feelings is not as easy, but someone can still make all the gains they need using EFT. The only difference is that their convincer experience can only be tested through the reality check on the "before" and "after" of the problem.

- The Problem Requires Perseverance

There are some people out there who should get a gold star for perseverance. They were introduced to EFT, saw how well it worked for others (or even found that it had worked well on a different problem), applied it to a new problem and nothing much happened. They then went on to keep at it, tapping day after day regardless of the fact that "it didn't seem to work".

Ten days later, and the problem was gone. There are many, many examples of this on the www.emofree.com website. We really don't know why this happens in a few cases, but seeing that EFT is free and doesn't take much time, I would strongly advise to "keep at it" if you find a problem doesn't budge right away.

Fail Safe Techniques

After these disclaimers, now on to a few things you can try to unblock a process when it seems to be stuck:

- Long Tap

Tapping a single main point persistently for fifty to a hundred times can sometimes bring about a major shift. You can muscle test for which point to use, or try various points for yourself. The Gamut point, the Karate Chop point, the Collar Bone point and the Under Eye point are good candidates to try.

- Break State

Sometimes it can be helpful to do something else for a short while and then come back to the problem. Often it will then respond to the tapping as normal. Getting up and marching on the spot, changing chairs, walking around for a short time, clapping briskly or just taking a "time out" can do the trick.

- Water

There are many theories as to why drinking water is so beneficial before, during and after energy work, but it certainly is worth trying if you are stuck in a process. Many therapists have their clients drink water during and after the session as a matter of course, so that's something you might like to experiment with.

- Collarbone Breathing

Hold the collarbone point with one hand, and then the Gamut spot on that hand with the other. Breathe half way in, then in completely, hold, breathe half way out, then out completely, hold and repeat three to seven times.

Swap over and do the other collar bone point/hand combination. Then resume the tapping on the problem at the point you were previously stuck.

- Extra Eye Movements

In the 9 Gamut procedure, notice when you move your eyes from side to side and around in a circle whether there are any areas where you (or your client) don't track smoothly, but make a small "jump". Go backwards and forwards over this "jump" until the eyes track smoothly all the way whilst holding or tapping the Gamut spot.

- Combination Points

Try tapping on or holding more than one point together at the same time. This can lead to some interesting shifts and sensations. Rubbing both

196

"sore spots" at the same time can be tried, or for example holding the Under Eye point with one hand and tapping on the Karate Chop point with the other. Stephanie Rothman suggests a "one man hug" whereby you cross your arms and hold both Under Arm points at the same time.

There are very many possible permutations, including hand positions that cover most of the facial points all at once.

- Someone Else's Energy

Every meridian therapist has had the occasional experience of watching a client tapping themselves and nothing much happens. We then tend to ask if the client minds if we may do the tapping for them, and very often the shift occurs within minutes, or even seconds.

I really don't know for sure why this happens; I have even had a personal experience of failing to get my usual shifts on a particular problem, calling in a friend and no sooner had they touched a couple of points, the emotion just disappeared.

I have a notion that this could have something to do with putting the same kind of energy back into the system that caused the problem in the first place. It doesn't happen very often and seems to be confined to certain types of "identity" problems; but should you get stuck somewhere, it's certainly well worth trying if "someone else's energy" flavour is required to get the breakthrough.

The Greatest Fail Safe Of The All:

"Keep At It!"

CONCLUSION

This section concludes the major part of this book. I sincerely hope you have come across some useful suggestions and some of the problems may have had a resonance for you; and I sincerely hope that you will be amongst those people who take this technique to heart, realise its incredible potential and really start to use is everywhere and anywhere there are limitations in your life.

One thing I would very much like to say to you before we conclude with the terminology & further reading section. I cannot know how many different therapies and techniques you have tried so far, and what or how severe your own personal problems are. What I do know is that many of us have been disappointed in the past with techniques that promised cures and help and then did not deliver or live up to our expectations.

As a result, we develop a deep rooted scepticism and cynicism about new treatments, to protect ourselves from further disappointment. I understand this perfectly because this is how I normally work. I am extremely cautious with new techniques and test them rigorously, even obsessively, before even considering to put my name to an endorsement. I also generally don't tend to write about other people's therapeutic techniques because I develop my own.

I have made an exception in the case of EFT because, in spite of my best efforts, I cannot say any other than that this truly works, at a deep physiological level, that it has profound effects on people's minds and bodies, and that it is predictable, replicable and absolutely real.

I have tested the BASIC EFT PROTOCOL as it comes with many, many kinds of people and all kinds of different problems, in person, over the telephone, on the radio, via email and in public demonstrations. I am still astonished, nearly three years later, that I STILL cannot fault the basic technique for its simplicity and truly amazing success rate, even when used by absolute amateurs.

In this spirit, I offer the basic technique of EFT to you, without adornments, changes, personalisations, add-ons or frills of any kind. If you wish, you can add those after you have become familiar with this wonderful thing that deserves acknowledgement.

And now, for the EFT pledge I have every client take after their treatment has been successfully concluded: "You have learned this wonderful technique, you have experienced first hand what it can do for you, and now, I want you to promise me something in return."

"???"

Keep On Using It.
Try it on Everything.
And Tell Everyone About It!

Apex Effect

The Apex Effect is a strange phenomenon in the meridian therapies, where someone successfully overcomes a problem, but won't or rather can't believe it's the EFT that was responsible; sometimes problems can be resolved so completely, that the person forgets ever having had the problem in the first place.

I've had personal experiences of this: one was a shop proprietor, who looked very unhappy and grey. When I asked her what the problem was, she said she had a headache and a bad ache in her back and neck from sitting behind the till on a stool all day. I treated her with EFT, and she cheered up, the pain went, and then said, "Oh it was just because you made me laugh." I remember being quite blown away by this notion - if I truly had that power, I'd sell my services to expensive private hospitals as a stand up comedian and pain reliever!

The other incident revolved around a student who had overcome a book phobia with my help. During a telephone check back session, he went on and on how helpful the EFT had been for his bowling scores, and never once mentioned the book phobia. When I asked about it, he had no recollection of the problem at all; when I pointed out to him that it was highly unlikely he would have scraped together the money for a session with a hypnotherapist to help with his bowling, he was completely flummoxed and very disturbed by his complete amnesia surrounding the book problem.

The apex effect can be intensely frustrating for practitioners; some tape their sessions so they can prove to their clients that they really did feel bad when they first arrived.

There is a school of thought that puts the Apex effect down to the actual changes that have occurred in someone's interactive energy systems during the treatment – as the systems find a new balance, there is a disruption in normal cognitive functioning for a short time.

Re-aligning the energy system with Reiki, Therapeutic Touch or similar techniques, and taking time to allow for a successful integration of the new learnings, insights, understandings and state of being help to combat the Apex effect.

The Discovery Statement

"The cause of all negative emotions is a disruption in the body's energy system."

Meridians

Apparently, the oldest maps of the body meridians are from Tibet and around 6000 years old.

Emotional blockages in the meridians have been likened to the effect of problems to that of rocks being placed into a brook - when you remove the rocks, the brook flows smoothly and cleanly.

According to a combined effort by Tom Bolton, Susan Courtney and Nick Harvard, the points used in EFT relate to the meridians like this:

Eyebrow

Inner Direction; EB = Eyebrow point = Bladder 2
When blocked increase fear and inhibition. After tapping releases fear and increases courage.

Corner Of Eye

Harmony; EC = Eye Corner = Gall Bladder 1
When blocked depletes energy. When tapped removes lethargy and re-enforces determination and courage.

Under Eye

Contentment; UE = Under Eye = Stomach 1
When blocked causes muddled thinking. When tapped releases indecisive emotions and increases the ability for intellectual and powerful thinking.

Under Nose
Inner Connection; UN = Under nose = Governing Vessel
Energy imbalance through physical disturbance, this meridian controls the body When blocked causes introversion. When tapped removes shyness and enhances the ability to communicated and form relationships with others and groups.

Under Mouth
Self Empowerment CH = Chin = Central Vessel (Conception Vessel)
Energy imbalance through emotions, this is the main controller of emotions. When blocked holds past traumatic emotions. When tapped releases pre-birth and birth trauma emotions, allowing CHI energy to circulate, strengthening and removing lethargy and fatigue.

Collarbone
Gentle Spirit; CB = Collarbone = Kidney Meridian
Energy imbalance through fears, esp. fears of what is unknown When blocked unable to make decisions low energy. When tapped gives impetus and willpower to carry out tasks.

Under Arm
Choice Making; UA = Under Arm = Spleen Meridian
Energy imbalance through resentment. When blocked slows down thinking processes. When tapped removes fogged thinking patterns and increases concentration.

Thumb
Worth; TH = Thumb = Lung Meridian
Energy imbalance through negative thinking. When blocked causes lethargy and low energy. When tapped releases negativity and increases vitality and positivity.

Index Finger
Letting Go; IF = Index Finger = Large Intestine Meridian
Energy imbalance through hanging on to grief and guilt. When blocked causes nostalgia. When tapped releases emotions that hold us to living in the past. Allows us to live in the present, be optimistic and work towards future goals.

Middle Finger
Bonding; MF = Middle Finger = Pericardium Meridian
Energy imbalance through being unhappy with self and others. When blocked produces feelings of low self esteem. When tapped releases feelings of inferiority and increases personal power.

Little Finger
Unconditional Love; LF = Little Finger = Heart Meridian
Energy imbalance through lack of love for self and others. When blocked results in selfishness and loneliness. When tapped removes limited thinking, opens up consciousness and improves long term memory. Aids the development of empathy, compassion and unconditional love.

Karate Chop Point
Trust; KS = Karate Spot = Small Intestine Meridian
When blocked it results in lack of confidence and feelings of self hate. When tapped removes self doubt, feelings of low self esteem and improves self-confidence.

Gamut Spot
Connection; GS = Gamut Spot = Triple Warmer (thyroid meridian) = When blocked inability to express emotions and love. When tapped removes low self esteem and opens us up to emotional interaction with others.

NB: If you have been taught about meridians and disagree with some of the placements or interpretations, don't worry.

There are many subtle differences according to which school of meridian therapy someone was trained in. The basic principles however, are the same and any differences in interpretations do not affect EFT treatments nor their outcome in any way. Indeed, knowing about meridians has no perceptible benefit in applying EFT treatments successfully.

Note: A good EFT workbook with "added meridian knowledge" is The Art & Science of Emotional Freedom by Ananga Sivyer, available from http://theamt.com

MET

MET stands for Meridian Energy Therapy and is the name for the whole field of these new techniques based on cognition PLUS working directly with the energy system. This includes EFT as well as TFT Thought Field Therapy, BSFF Be Set Free Fast, TAT Tapas Acupressure Technique and numerous other techniques besides.

Opening Statement

The "Even though I have this problem, I deeply and profoundly love and accept myself" start up declaration at the beginning of each round of EFT.

Opening Statements can be positive as well as negative: "I want to be really happy and I deeply and profoundly accept myself". This form is used when major blocks have already been removed to support the general healing process, to keep a client focussed on a particular outcome, or when it is not appropriate to be looking for root causes.

It often happens that resistance reveals itself during the course of tapping a positive statement which can then be dealt with.

Proxy Tapping/Surrogate Tapping

A very unusual feature of the Energy Therapies is that they can be applied by one person for another.

Often used when there is distance involved, or the recipient is unconscious or cannot tap for themselves, and in the case of small babies, Tapping By Proxy is highly effective. To put the effectiveness into perspective, we're not talking about praying or absent healing here. Something physical takes place about 8 times out of 10 in the recipient of the treatment; this knocks most every form of esoteric healing into a cocked hat.

How do you tap by proxy?
1. Make a statement of intent first: I AM (insert name of recipient), and then proceed with the opening statement and the treatment round as normal, noting any energy shifts as usual; so, for example, if you were

tapping for your friend James, you could say, "I am James. Even though I have a fear of heights, I deeply and profoundly accept myself".

2. Use this form of statement (which is highly recommended for children, pets, and others with whom you have a close and intimate relationship): "Even though James is afraid of heights, I deeply and profoundly accept him and love him."

In any problem situation that involves relationships of any kind, proxy tapping can be of great help; if there's two reasonably consenting humans involved, the shifts can be absolutely dramatic.

A recent case involving proxy tapping had a grandfather tap himself for the problems of his severely disabled granddaughter every night before he went to bed and whilst looking at her photograph.

The girl was seven years old and had suffered oxygen deprivation at birth; she could neither talk nor walk and suffered from fits. About a week after he started the proxy tapping, the girl said her first words ever. There is a mountain of anecdotal evidence from people all around the world who report similar success stories resulting from tapping a loved one by proxy.

This is a most fascinating aspect of EFT and one which I strongly invite you to explore for yourself - it cannot hurt and it can be absolutely astonishing in its results. (see also EFT & Pets in the A-Z)

Psychological Reversal

The flow of energy through the meridians is reversed through shock or intense fear and literally causes the opposite of what the owner of the meridians intends.

PR can be overridden with will power, but this is problematic and usually not a satisfactory long-term solution.

Rubbing the Sore Spot and/or tapping on the Karate Chop point corrects psychological reversal and so this is built into the EFT technique to make sure that if there is any PR, it is automatically corrected.

Round

One set of tapping all the body and finger points, from the top of the eyebrow to the karate chop point.

Sandwich

A Round, 9 Gamut Procedure, followed by another Round.

Session

A full EFT treatment set for a particular presenting problem that may consist of a number of rounds for different opening statements and aspects, all the way through to testing that all has been successfully resolved. Not to be confused with the "50 minute therapy hour" as there is no time limit either way.

Set Up

Rubbing either the Sore Spot, or the Karate Chop Point to remove any possible Psychological Reversal, saying the opening statement or using any of the other suggested methods to get in contact with the problem as directly as possible.

Shift

A physical sensation that is usually also noticeable to onlookers - something has happened and the person breathes more easily, feels lighter and better, and has experienced a profound reduction in their presenting symptoms.

Shortcut

Instead of tapping the entire round or sandwich, just some points are tapped to speed up the procedure. Some practitioners can intuit shortcuts after a while and there are advanced trainings which teach ways how to find shortcuts.

You can make your own shortcuts for an ongoing problem by stating the problem and lightly touching each one of the points.

The points that feels strange, different or tender are the ones that will become your personal shortcut for that particular issue.

SUDs Scale

Subjective Units of Disturbance - for another to understand how painful/uncomfortable something is to a particular person on a scale of 0-10, and to be able to track subtle changes easily. Also sometimes referred to as Subjective Units of Distress or Discomfort.

VOC Scale

Validity Of Cognition, or in other words, to rate how true one believes something to be. In the strictly clinical psychology way, the VOC scale has only seven subdivisions between completely true and completely untrue; I just use ten like the SUDs scale, it's less confusing.

PART VI - EFT RESOURCES

EFT is a child of the Internet.

If you have access to a computer, there is a world of information available on websites, chat lists and newsgroups and their archives.

An excellent first introduction for someone who has never heard of EFT is
http://123EFT.com

More in depth information on EFT can be found on Gary Craig's home site
www.emofree.com

Spanish Language EFT and MET information is available from
http://tecnicas-tapping.com (also Spanish Language Version of this book in hard copy and ebook)

German Language EFT and MET information is available from
http://emofree.de

German Language Version of this book is available from
http://emotionale-freiheit.com

Full catalogue of trainings and manuals by Silvia Hartmann, including more advanced Energy Therapies, available from
http://starfields.org

The Association For Meridian Energy Therapies

The AMT has more advanced information on EFT and hundreds of articles and downloads on METs in general, as well as an online ebook store, two newsgroups, an acclaimed MET practitioner certification programme, trainings and conference listings and World Wide referrals/contacts on http://TheAMT.com

About The Author

Silvia Hartmann PhD is a highly qualified and experienced trainer of Hypnosis, Hypnotherapy, Energy Therapies and Neuro-Linguistic Programming, author, international lecturer and motivational speaker. She is the Co-Founder and Director of The Association For Meridian & Energy Therapies and founder of the oldest established MET internet newsgroup, Meridiantherapy, as well as being a Contributing Editor to Gary Craig's EmoFree List.

With an extensive record in trainings design, she is well known for her outstanding ability to create trainings that allow the participants to understand and integrate even highly complex materials and making it easy to learn, easy to do and easy to replicate.

She is the author of numerous highly acclaimed original works in the field, including "Project Sanctuary" and "Guiding Stars 2002".

Silvia Hartmann's best-selling EFT Training Manual "Adventures In EFT" has to date been translated into four languages and is acknowledged to be "The Best Book on EFT".

After studying and re-searching Energy Psychology & Meridian Energy Therapies approaches in-depth for four years, Silvia Hartmann created EmoTrance™, a truly groundbreaking and entirely innovative approach to working with the human energy system for mental and physical health.

For Further Information about Silvia's Work please visit:

http://sidereus.org - News & Library Portal Of The Sidereus Foundation

http://starfields.org - Complete Online Catalogue of Manuals & Trainings

http://dragonrising.com - Hard Copy Books, Courses, CDs etc.

http://emotrance.com - The EmoTrance™ News & Library Portal

Adventures In EFT

Adventures In EFT is the World's best selling guide for beginners to Gary Craig's Emotional Freedom Techniques EFT.

Now in its fifth revised edition, Adventures does not require any previous knowledge of healing, counselling, psychology or human health or changework at all – anyone who can read can pick up this book and start to make their lives feel a whole lot better, right away.

Yet, in spite of Adventures' easy to read, friendly and informative style, all the base patterns of EFT are here – modelled on Gary Craig himself and with additional modelling from the leading EFT therapists in the World, Adventures is also a fine handbook for any healer or counsellor wishing to begin to make use of the extraordinary powers of EFT to make profound changes in people's lives.

Sparkling with ideas, enthusiasm and lively suggestions for how to take the Classic EFT protocols and make them come to life for you.

Adventures In EFT
The Essential Field Guide To
Emotional Freedom Techniques
by Silvia Hartmann, PhD
ISBN 1 873483 63 5

Available from
http://DragonRising.com - 44 1323 729 666
and all good bookshops.

The Advanced Patterns Of EFT

Primarily for professional therapists, psychologists and students and researchers in the field of Meridian & Energy Therapies, The Advanced Patterns of EFT by Silvia Hartmann, PhD, re-writes the limits of what used to be.

The first part of this advanced manual concentrates on mastery in the EFT treatment flow and describes essential patterns, techniques and variations on the Classic EFT process which move an EFT treatment into the realms of true quantum healing.

The second part consists of the advanced patterns themselves – treatment guides, techniques and approaches for guilt, bereavement, high end addictions, parts healing, shamanic applications and the original Guiding Stars patterns, released for the first time.

The Advanced Patterns Of EFT is an outstanding, original contribution to the emergent field of Meridian & Energy Therapies and an invaluable resource to any serious student, practitioner and researcher in the field.

The Advanced Patterns Of EFT
by Silvia Hartmann, PhD
ISBN 1 873483 68 6

Available from
http://DragonRising.com - 44 1323 729 666
and all good bookshops.

For most people, EFT is all they could ask for and all they ever need to smooth out their lives and be able to do and be so much more than they ever thought possible.

I've learned so much by working with EFT this closely for four years, and as a result of what I have learned, I have designed EmoTrance – a stand-alone Energy Healing system for those who wish to work with the human energy body in a more personal, more intimate way.

EmoTrance™ re-connects the user with their bodies and their own being in a profound and lasting way. It is an outstanding self help tool not just to remove old injuries but also to manage new states that arise all the time, there and then, so they need never become future incidents for us to have to tap on.

EmoTrance™ is further a superb healing technique when a healer and a client align in their intention to produce a change – entirely client driven, entirely respectful of one individual human's personal perceptions and experiences in this World, it is fast, gentle and deeply profound in all applications.

Lastly, EmoTrance™ is designed to teach us about our own intuition, our own energy systems and that of others, our "energy nutritional requirements" and what energy healing really is at the end of the day.

If you have worked with EFT and you are ready to step beyond into a whole new world of living today and creating tomorrow, we invite you to take a closer look.

Oceans Of Energy

The Patterns & Techniques Of EmoTrance™ Volume 1

by Silvia Hartmann, PhD

ISBN 1 873483 73 2

Available from
http://DragonRising.com - 44 1323 729 666
and all good bookshops.

Project Sanctuary III

So now, we are working with the energy body, with thoughtfields, with meridians and energy shields and in the Quantum spaces where what we have learned about time, gravity, distance and more is no longer applicable. If we go into those spaces with our limited four-dimensional thinking, formed by the cause-and-effects of the physicality and after a lifetime of conditioning in the Hard, we will never be able to be at home here, never be able to actually **understand** and never mind affect these spaces and their processes as we should and as we can.

What is required is to learn a whole new way of thinking.

A logic based on entirely different principles, on entirely different laws of nature – quantum logic. Project Sanctuary is probably the first training manual ever written in the history of humanity to be a self help guide and device to teach quantum logic and to make it easy for anyone who wishes to learn.

Fascinating from the start, utilising immediately what we have remaining by the way of connection to our intuition, creativity, magic and the wider realms of the universe, Project Sanctuary is easy.

Indeed, it is surprisingly easy and what so many find so much more surprising still is the fact that this is not head-hurting school learning at all but exciting, fun, stimulating, sexy, funny, breath-takingly amazing and on occasion frighteningly exciting, too.

And that IS our first lesson in quantum logic – FORGET about learning being difficult or painful. FORGET THAT. That was learning the hard way and you can't learn hard amidst the flowing, glowing vibrant oceans of energy from which we came, and to which we will return in glory and delight, a homecoming of such wonder and awe, it will take your breath away.

For anyone seriously interested in getting really serious about learning, it's time to seriously lighten up and start learning for yourself, by yourself, in yourself – a one-on-one tuition between you and the universe itself. Project Sanctuary is your manual, handbook and tour guide - if you want it.

Project Sanctuary III

by Silvia Hartmann, PhD

ISBN 1 873483 98 8

Available from
http://DragonRising.com - 44 1323 729 666
and all good bookshops.

Certification Trainings In Meridian & Energy Therapies

The METs (which include EFT) are a whole new form of working with human mind-body problems. This being so, and in recognition of the fact that MET practitioners derive from all and every helping profession, allopathic and holistic, psychologists and body workers, hypnotherapists and healers, nurses and social workers included, the syllabus of the AMT Practitioner training includes essential knowledge of the protocols and practical hands on procedures in this new healing field.

Co-developed by the founder trainers of The AMT and trainings designed by Silvia Hartmann, PhD, the AMT Certification trainings represent state-of-the-art professional training which cannot be had elsewhere.

Silvia Hartmann also developed a correspondence course version of the live AMT training in order to open the possibility of gaining the benefits from this professional training to those who cannot personally attend a training.

To find a certified AMT practitioner or advanced practitioner, or for a list of training events, please go to http://theamt.com

Certified Practitioner/Certified Advanced Practitioner

Of Meridian & Energy Therapies

Professional Live Trainings & Distance Trainings

The Association For Meridian & Energy Therapies The AMT

http://TheAMT.com

Order The AMT Yearbook

Trainers & Practitioners Registers

Meridian & Energy Therapies Books

Events, Conferences & Organisations

Who's Who In Meridian Energy Therapies

EFT, TFT, TAT, ET, BSFF, HBLU, CHART, EDxTM

The Essential Guide To The New Energy Therapies

Available from
http://DragonRising.com - 44 1323 729 666
and all good bookshops.

Adventures In EFT
6th Edition - UK